Henry Hill Hickn.....
by Dr W.D.A. Smith

HENRY HICKMAN, MRCS, was born on 27th January 1800. He died on 2nd April 1830. The reproduction on the cover is of the only known surviving portrait painted in his time (in oils 750 x 600mm) was taken from a photograph generously donated by Dr W.G.H. Leslie, a direct descendant, and supplied by the Hickman Society. In a letter dated 5th January 1911, Mrs H.C. Bettridge, one of Henry Hickman's granddaughters, wrote to Mr C.J.S. Thompson, Curator of the Wellcome Historical Medical Museum:

> *I have had the oil painting of my grandfather carefully packed (by a picture man) and insured ... and forwarded to you today (Friday) to the address you gave me and I trust that every care will be taken of the picture and that it will be delivered to me as soon as possible...*

Evidently the portrait meant a lot to her. Mrs Bettridge added...

> *...the hands are not quite finished... after the face, and upper part was complete, some little time elapsed before my grandfather thought he would be able to give another sitting; during this time he was taken ill and was never able after to sit again for the picture to be finished - so it was really painted in the last year of his life...*

Yours very truly
H.C. Bettridge.

The painting was restored in 1984 by Mr Bertram Charles Whittle, of Hawks Hill Gallery, Western Australia. The same year he was commissioned to paint a copy, which is now at the Royal College of Anaesthetists, London.

Comment [WDAS]
The wording: *Some little time elapsed before my grandfather thought he would be able to give another sitting...* seems to imply that the sittings had to be arranged well in advance and they probably took place away from home (for example, perhaps Worcester, Wolverhampton or Birmingham but not as far away as Paris). The artist is unknown.

Cover below the Portrait: The Brass Door Plate from Hickman's surgery in Ludlow.
Courtesy of the Science Museum/Science & Society Picture Library.

© The History of Anaesthesia Society

ISBN 0-901100-59-5

Designed and printed by J. W. Northend Limited,
Clyde Road, Sheffield S8 0TZ
Tel 0114 250 0331 Fax 0114 250 0676
ks@northend.co.uk

Contents

Preface
Histories of Anaesthesia

Before the Second World War articles on the history of anaesthesia were generally short, until Fülöp-Miller led in another direction with the publication of his book *Triumph Over Pain*[1]; Beinart listed a further six titles. The literature on anaesthesia suggests that relatively little interest was shown in its history by anaesthetists in the United Kingdom until the end of the Second World War. Their interest in the history of anaesthesia is very much alive today as evidenced by the success of five international symposia (1982, 1987, 1992, 1997, 2001). The second was held at the Royal College of Surgeons of England and all its delegates bar one were anaesthetists. They did not claim to be more than amateur historians. The exception was Jennifer Beinart.

This quote is from a paper read by Jennifer Beinart at the Second International Symposium on the History of Anaesthesia, in 1987[2].

Denis Smith.
*Supplied by Editors of
the History of Anaesthesia
Society Proceedings.*

> *Although we cannot all be concerned with the same problems, I feel that we should all attempt to set our research into a wider context. It is rather as though each of us was digging away, to uncover our own piece of mosaic; we need to step back in order to see the whole pattern.*

I have tried to step back.

Hickman began his experiments on suspended animation around 1823, more than 20 years before the discovery of general anaesthesia using nitrous oxide and ether. Hickman was clearly a pioneer but his leads were neither understood nor followed. What drew my attention to Hickman were suggestions that he used nitrous oxide[1,3,4,5] but I found no corroborative evidence. In 1982 when re-publishing articles on the history of nitrous oxide and oxygen anaesthesia, I reserved material concerning Hickman for this biography[6,7,8,9]. The story of Hickman, as retold here by a retired anaesthetist, includes the transition from surgical operations without anaesthesia to those without pain. It is as much a partial pre-history of anaesthesia as it is a superficial biography of a pioneer of anaesthesia. It is intended for people interested in the history of anaesthesia, surgery and medicine with local histories of Shropshire, Worcestershire and Herefordshire where Hickman spent most of his short life. In presenting evidence I aim to distinguish between fact, fiction, guesswork, assumption and misapprehension. I try to get close to Hickman and to stand back. I set him against various backgrounds using perspectives extending far beyond his own four-dimensional boundaries. Guesswork has helped to identify and to frame valid questions but I try to avoid using conjecture as if it were something more concrete. In general I aim to present what is known about Hickman and how it came to be known, together with undisguised speculation about the unknown. Past publications are reviewed, fresh avenues explored and others suggested, but coverage is limited. Duncum's example of enlivening text with quotations has been followed[10]. It allows witnesses opportunities to speak for themselves with minimum distortion of original meaning that may occur when resorting to precis, paraphrase or circumlocution. Opinions about Hickman depend upon the evidence selected, its interpretation and the skill of its presentation. They depend also upon similar factors in the reader such as his or her reading skills, knowledge, experience, bias, interest, and imagination. For better or worse, readers contribute something to or detract from what they read. The narrative was originally planned in three parts linked by limited cross-references and a little repetition. As the book grew its weight and the nature of its content pressed it into less easily defined shapes. Some items were repositioned others would have been presented differently had there been more time.

References

1. Fülöp-Miller R. *Triumph Over Pain*. Translated by Eden & Cedar Paul. London: Hamish Hamilton 1938.

2. Beinart J. *Problems and sources in the history of anaesthesia*. In: Atkinson R.S., Boulton T.B., editors. *The History of Anaesthesia; Proceedings of the Second International Symposium on the History of Anaesthesia* held in London 20-23 July 1987. London: Royal Society of Medicine Services Limited and Carnforth: Parthenon Publishing Group Limited 1989.

3. Boyle H.E.G. Nitrous oxide: history and development. *Brit. Med. J.* 1934; **i**: 153.

4. Duran C.M. From the abyss of pain to the summit. *J. Hist. Med.* 1946; **i**: 665.

5. Prescott F. *The Control of Pain*. London: English Universities Press. 1964.

6. Smith W.D.A. A history of nitrous oxide and oxygen anaesthesia Part IV: Hickman and the introduction of certain gases into the lungs. *Brit. J. Anaesth.* 1966; **38**: 58.

7. Smith W.D.A. A history of nitrous oxide and oxygen anaesthesia Parts VIA & VIB: Further light on Hickman and his time. *Brit. J. Anaesth.* 1970; **42**: 347 & 445.

8. Smith W.D.A. A history of nitrous oxide and oxygen anaesthesia Parts IVC VID & VIE: Henry Hill Hickman in his time. *Brit. J. Anaesth.* 1978; **50**: 519, 623 & 853.

9. Smith W.D.A. *Under the Influence: a History of Nitrous Oxide and Oxygen Anaesthesia*. London and Basingstoke: Macmillan/Chicago: Wood Library-Museum. 1982: p. xiii.

10. Duncum B.M. *The Development of Inhalation Anaesthesia with special reference to the years 1846-1900* London: Wellcome Historical Medical Museum and Oxford University Press 1947. 2nd ed. London: Royal Society of Medicine Press Ltd on behalf of the History of Anaesthesia Society 1994.

11. Smith W.D.A. Surgery without pain; background. *Anaesth. & Int. Care* 1986; **14**: 70-78.

12. Smith W.D.A. Surgery without pain; Part II 1800-1847. *Anaesth. & Int. Care* 1986; **14**: 186-191.

Foreword

A prolific writer on anaesthesia and related subjects, W.D.A (Denis) Smith died in 2002 aged 84. The life and times of Henry Hill Hickman had been of absorbing interest to him and several of his papers on this pioneer of anaesthesia were published in the *British Journal of Anaesthesia* and the Australian journal: *Anaesthesia and Intensive Care* between 1966 and 1986 [6,7,8,9,11,12].

During more recent years it is clear that Denis was working on a magnum opus – an extensive history of the search for relief of operative pain and suffering throughout the ages. He focussed on Hickman's vision and experimental development of inhalational anaesthesia in the 1820s, followed by his failure to convince anyone in Britain or France of the potential of the method. His attempts preceded by some 20 years the final breakthrough in the United States of America in the 1840s. Denis's original manuscript runs to over 800 pages and is a remarkable assembly of thought and work on the evolution of anaesthesia in the Western World. It was in the possession of Hickman's descendants who kindly made it available to the History of Anaesthesia Society. Their help and encouragement in the preparation of this booklet is gratefully acknowledged, as is the co-operation of Mrs Sheila Barlow, Denis's secretary who kindly provided computer discs of much of this material. Much as the publication seemed desirable to the author's family and members of the History of Anaesthesia Society, it proved impossible to finance a project of this size. However, lack of recognition of Hickman and his life and work in his own country seemed to demand wider awareness of Denis's detailed and extensive research.

A small group of members of the Society decided to select sections of the original manuscript of greatest relevance to Hickman and combined them to form this book. It must be emphasised that great care was taken to retain as far as possible Denis's original style and wording so that the authorship of the publication can be rightly ascribed to him and form a tribute to his lifetime devotion to anaesthesia and pain relief. What follows, is the editors' humble efforts for which they alone are responsible.

Dr Adrian Padfield, Dr Edward Armitage, Dr Frank Bennetts and Dr Peter Drury.

Acknowledgements

Denis's manuscripts contained two sides of acknowledgements about two chapters only, most of them obscure to the editors. We are in no position to acknowledge the many people who gave him help and can only apologise for this omission. We would, however, like to acknowledge the help of several individuals not mentioned in our Foreword above.

Dr Adrian Kuipers, member of HAS and the Hickman Society, who has been tireless taking photographs for the book.

Dr Carole Reeves, of the Wellcome Trust Medical Photographic Library for showing us the great range of Hickman images held by that Library.

Mr John Greenhill of the Tenbury Museum for his help and providing copies of the Centenary Invitation and the miniature of Eliza, Hickman's wife.

The staff at Ludlow Museum for their help and the copy of the 1824 Auction Notice.

List of Illustrations

Significant Events in Hickman's Life

1800 27th January	Hickman born at Lady Halton.
1800 30th January	Baptised 'Henry Hickman' at Bromfield.
1804 14th January	Eliza Hannah Gardner baptised at Cotheridge, near Worcester.
1816-18	Hickman began entries in his Notebook No. 2. and was probably apprenticed to Jukes & Watson of Stourport-on-Severn.
1818 19th-31st January	Attended Brookes' Anatomy Course; London.
1819 21st September	Hickman wrote to Eliza from Edinburgh.
1819 1st November	Hickman matriculated at Edinburgh, No. 269.
1819-1820	Hickman a student at Edinburgh University for six months.
1819 19th November	Hickman signed laws of Royal Medical Society *(Edinburgh student body)*.
1820 5th May	Diploma of the Royal College of Surgeons, London (MRCS).
1820/1821 May-Feb	Probably set up in practice in Ludlow during these nine months.
1821 23rd February	Advertisement for an apprentice in the *Shrewsbury Chronicle*, almost certainly inserted by Hickman. (Repeated on 9th, 16th, 23rd and 30th March)(also in 1823).
1821 21st June	Henry Hickman married Miss E.H. Gardner of Leigh Court near Worcester.
1821 17th August	*Shrewsbury Chronicle* published a letter from a grateful patient, praising Hickman. Signed 'C.N.'.
1821 September	H.H. Hickman published a case history and post-mortem in the *London Medical Repository* **16** p.202.
1822/1823	Hickman, Henry listed in *Pigot's Shropshire Directory* in Corve Street, Ludlow, under SURGEONS.
20th March 1823/22/21?	Possible dates for first recorded experiments.
1823 13th October	Mrs Gardner wrote to her daughter Eliza.
1823 7th November	Annotation in the *Shrewsbury Chronicle* referred to 'Museum of Dr. Hickman of Ludlow, in this county' and to Dr Hickman's 'paper on the Monstrosity of the Foetus'.
1823/4	Parents-in-law left Leigh Court to join their son, Benjamin, at 'The Hyde', a farm about two miles away.
1824 21st February	Handwritten letter from Hickman to T.A. Knight Esq.; describing his animal experiments on surgical operations during suspended animation.
1824 24th-26th May	'Property of Mr Henry Hickman who is leaving Ludlow'. Auctioned by J. Bach.
1824 14th August	Hickman had printed in Shifnal: *A Letter on Suspended Animation ...addressed to T. A. Knight, Esq. of Downton Castle, Herefordshire.*
1824 30th November	Mrs Gardner buried at Stanford Bishop.
1824 1st December	Hickman's first child, Elizabeth Catherine, baptised Stanford Bishop (born at The Hyde).
1825 3rd June	Much of his Pamphlet reproduced in the *Shrewsbury Chronicle*.
1825 Jan-June	Hickman's Pamphlet reviewed in *The Gentleman's Magazine*.
1826 26th January	Acted as Steward at Annual Charity Ball at Jerningham Arms, Shifnal.
1826 4th February	Hickman and Pamphlet severely criticised in a letter to *The Lancet* signed 'Antiquack'.
1828 21st April	Hickman wrote to his wife from Paris.
1828 31st July	Hickman purchased a bracelet for his wife in the Palais Royale.
1828 7th August	Receipt acknowledged of Hickman's Memorial to Charles X King of France.
1828 31st August	The Memorial forwarded to Académie Royale de Médicine.
1828 28th September	The Memorial considered at a meeting of the Académie.
1828 10th November	Hickman gave the bracelet to his wife at the Hotel Meurice, Paris.
1829 11th September	Hickman's fourth child, Mary, baptised at Tenbury.
1830 2nd April	Hickman died at Tenbury.
1830 5th April	Buried at Bromfield.

CHAPTER ONE

A Brief Biography

Henry Hill Hickman was an English pioneer of inhalation anaesthesia. He was born in the Shropshire hamlet of Lady Halton in the parish of Bromfield in 1800 and was baptised in the parish church of St. Mary the Virgin. He practised in the vicinity for ten years, died at Tenbury Wells in 1830 and was buried in the family grave at Bromfield.

Born a farmer's son, Hickman obtained the diploma of membership of the Royal College of Surgeons of England (MRCS) in 1820 and became a country practitioner, first in Ludlow, then in Shifnal and finally in Tenbury. Between leaving Shifnal and setting up practice in Tenbury he visited Paris partly to seek help with his experiments, in which he claimed to have demonstrated in animals the possibility of rendering patients insensible during surgery. Hickman wrote that while performing his surgical duties he frequently lamented that something had not been thought of:

whereby the fears may be tranquillized and suffering relieved.

He went on to say:

Above all, from the many experiments on suspended animation I have wondered that some hint has not been thrown out, of its probable utility, and noticed by Surgeons.

It is sometimes assumed that Hickman's ideas for preventing acute surgical distress must have arisen primarily from observations during surgery, but he may also have owed much to contemporary interest in suffocation, the inhalation of noxious gases, drowning and suspended animation. The particular experiments to which he referred have not been identified, but it is known that Benjamin Collins Brodie had administered both carbonic acid (gas) and ether to guinea pigs as early as 1821[1] (Chapter 3).

Hickman himself experimented with a variety of small animals, denying them fresh air or giving them carbon dioxide to breathe, in both cases inducing a reversible state of insensibility, which he equated with 'suspended animation'. By performing surgical operations upon them while they were in this state he demonstrated the possibility of pain-free surgery in small animals. We do not know whether anyone other than Hickman witnessed any of his experiments. He described them in a handwritten paper dated 21st February 1824, which he addressed to T.A. Knight Esq. (1759-1838) of Downton Castle, Herefordshire (Chapter 5). Knight was a Fellow of the Royal Society, and Downton Castle was about two miles from Lady Halton. A version of Hickman's handwritten paper survives. Six months later a longer version of this letter was printed as a pamphlet (Chapter 5), but judging by its extreme rarity, few copies were distributed. The only original extant print is held by the Wellcome Trust.

There is no record of Hickman having experimented with suspended animation in humans though presumably that was in mind when, in 1828, he visited Paris. At the end of his pamphlet he volunteered that he would be prepared to become the subject of an experiment if he should find himself under the necessity of suffering any long or severe operation. Hickman appealed to Charles X, King of France for patronage. He explained that he visited Paris:

> *in part for the purpose of bringing to completion a discovery, to which [he had been] led by a course of observations and experiments on suspended animation...*

His appeal continued:

> *It appears demonstrable that the hitherto most agonising, dangerous and delicate surgical operations, may now be performed, with perfect safety, and exemption from pain, on brute animals in a state of suspended animation. Hence it is to be strongly inferred, by analogy, that the same salutary effects may be produced on the human frame, when rendered insensible by means of the introduction of certain gases into the lungs...*

Hickman sought permission of Charles X, King of France:

> *to develop [his] ideas on operations in a state of suspended animation, in the presence of [His] Majesty's Medical and Surgical schools, that [he might] have the benefit of their eminent and assembled talent and emulous co-operation* (Chapter 6 and Appendix A).

Hickman's letter was forwarded to the *Académie Royal de Médecine* where it was said to have been ridiculed. He returned to England and died two months after his 30th birthday. The whole episode was soon forgotten. By 1847, shortly after the discovery of ether anaesthesia in America, the only Englishman publicly to admit awareness of Hickman's experiments was Thomas Dudley of Kingswinford and he appears not to have taken part in them (Chapter 8). Dudley (1805-1865) was a layman about five years Hickman's junior who spoke up for him through letters to *The Lancet* and to the *Medical Times*[2], reinforced by correspondence with Hickman's widow[3].

Little more was heard of Hickman until 1911 when C.J.S. Thompson, the first Curator of the Wellcome Historical Medical Museum, obtained some of Hickman's important manuscripts[4], but what directed Thompson's attention to Hickman in the first place is obscure. The renewed interest in Hickman barely survived the First World War. Not until the centenary of his death drew near was the interest of the medical fraternity rekindled at the instigation of the Rev. F. Wayland Joyce, Rector of Burford, near Tenbury Wells*. Since then, memories of Hickman have been kept alive by occasional mentions in the literature and, from 1935, by the award of a Hickman Medal. The Medal was funded by subscription and is awarded every third year by the Council of the Royal Society of Medicine upon the recommendation of its Section of Anaesthesia…

> *…for original work of outstanding merit in anaesthesia, or in a subject directly connected therewith…to any person of any nationality…not necessarily medical….*

It is an imaginatively conceived award, which acknowledges merit in Hickman and in the Medallists. Its very existence may have helped to promote excellence in the practice

---

The Rev. F. Wayland Young was a local man. He followed his father as Rector of Burford on the River Teme about a mile west of Tenbury. He later became Dean of St. Paul's and in 1931 wrote 'A History of Tenbury Wells' where he died in 1934.

of anaesthesia and to have drawn attention to the need for support of research and for interdisciplinary and international co-operation. When the first Hickman Medal was awarded in 1935, the Association of Anaesthetists of Great Britain and Ireland had been in existence for only three years and Dr R.R. Macintosh (later Professor Sir Robert) was not appointed to the first Chair of Anaesthetics in the United Kingdom until 1937. Twenty-three Hickman Medals had been awarded by 2005 (Appendix D).

'Now' and 'Then'

Those of today's patients who are not embroiled in war or civil strife do not expect torture during surgery. They take it for granted that they will be made 'insensible' by means of general anaesthesia, except when the site of operation is deadened by nerve block. Five or six generations ago, however, general anaesthesia, as we know it, was not available and local anaesthesia did not emerge until the 1880s. Severe pain during surgery seemed inevitable so operations were to be avoided whenever possible. Accumulation of surgical experience must have been correspondingly slow.

The watershed between surgical operations with pain and those without is usually defined by the date: 16th October 1846, when W.T.G. Morton (1819-1868), an American dentist, gave the first public demonstration of ether anaesthesia in Boston, Massachusetts. Up to that time, awake patients often had to be held down while nightmarish operations were performed with speed and resolution, the victims doubtless wishing their surgeons would either stop or make even greater haste. It seemed to be taken for granted that there was no other way of coping with inevitable surgical pain, except by keeping knives and scissors sharp and operating with speed. Rooms used for surgery in patients' homes and in operating theatres (to which the public might be admitted) must have seemed like torture chambers. The tortured, unless they fainted, might yell without constraint or groan or, with teeth and fists tightly clenched, remain stoically but painfully silent. Afterwards they might nurse their physical and mental traumata with moans or silence. Soon after 1846 many, but not all, surgical patients were saved from such suffering[5]. Their surgeons were spared the horrors of inflicting it and could take more time, care and thought while operating quietly upon relatively immobile and relaxed patients who, once they were settled, hardly moved. Apart from any restraint required during induction of anaesthesia, they did not have to be held down.

Hickman's idea of putting patients into the 'torpid state' of 'suspended animation' before operating upon them presaged anaesthesia. In his pamphlet, he assured his readers that he had not written it in 'self-adulation', but as a duty incumbent on him as a medical practitioner and servant to the public...

> ...to make known any thing which has not been tried, and which ultimately may add something towards the relief of human suffering, arising from acute disease. The only method of obtaining this end is... candid discussion, and liberality of sentiment.

Hickman's stated hope was to tranquilize fear and diminish the agony. He claimed to have performed painless, safe and successful experimental surgery in puppies, dogs, mice, a rabbit and a kitten, after enclosing them temporarily within a glass cover to which he either prevented the access of fresh air or, slightly more often, admitted carbon dioxide. Those were his known methods of 'suspending animation' in 1824, but in the opening sentence of his pamphlet he referred to:

> The facility of suspending animation, by carbonic acid gas and other means...

Although carbon dioxide has its dangers there is no doubt that inhaling it can produce anaesthesia[6]. Hickman admitted that he could not conscientiously recommend a patient to risk his life in the experiment, but he was sufficiently confident to write that he:

> *certainly should not hesitate a moment to become the subject of it, ... under the necessity of suffering any long or severe operation.*

In 1828, having failed to gain any support for his ideas in England, he took the step, which surely must have been exceptional, of appealing to the King of France for the collaboration of 'His Majesty's Medical and Surgical Schools' (Chapter 6). Hickman's whole approach was open. Whereas Morton later attempted to conceal ether's identity under the name 'Letheon', and to patent it, Hickman, so far as is known, at least up to 1824, made no attempt to disguise his methods. The first half of Hickman's life was during the Napoleonic Wars and the second half in their aftermath; his professional life coincided with the reign of George IV (1820-1830). He spent a short time in Edinburgh and then in London at least long enough to pass the examination for diploma of Membership of the Royal College of Surgeons of England. He probably set up practice in Ludlow, Shropshire, between obtaining his MRCS in May 1820 and advertising for an apprentice in February 1821 *(figure 1)*. The first experiment reported in his handwritten letter to Knight was dated 20th March: most likely in 1823, but it could have been in 1822 or even 1821. In May 1824, about the time he left Ludlow for Shifnal (Shropshire), he auctioned his furniture and a collection of stuffed birds and animals *(figure 5, p34)*. His pamphlet is dated 14th August 1824, from Shifnal. The dates of the few notices of

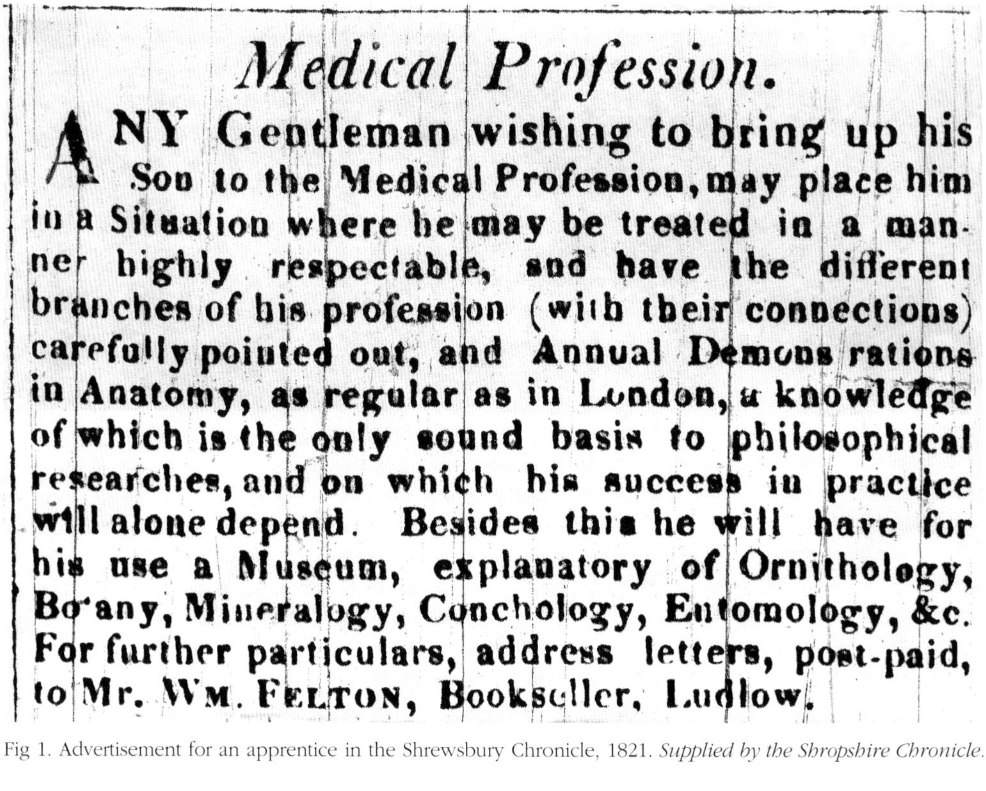

Medical Profession.

ANY Gentleman wishing to bring up his Son to the Medical Profession, may place him in a Situation where he may be treated in a manner highly respectable, and have the different branches of his profession (with their connections) carefully pointed out, and Annual Demonstrations in Anatomy, as regular as in London, a knowledge of which is the only sound basis to philosophical researches, and on which his success in practice will alone depend. Besides this he will have for his use a Museum, explanatory of Ornithology, Botany, Mineralogy, Conchology, Entomology, &c. For further particulars, address letters, post-paid, to Mr. WM. FELTON, Bookseller, Ludlow.

Fig 1. Advertisement for an apprentice in the Shrewsbury Chronicle, 1821. *Supplied by the Shropshire Chronicle.*

the pamphlet's publication suggest that it was probably distributed around June 1825. Hickman travelled to Paris from Shifnal to make his remarkable approach to the French Monarch in 1828. Finally, he moved to Tenbury Wells, Worcestershire, where he died soon after his thirtieth birthday.

No evidence has been found that Hickman directly influenced the discovery of anaesthesia, but he appeared to be working in that direction. How his story would have developed and ended had he lived longer is an open question. Those who were immediately involved in the introduction of ether anaesthesia lived barely a generation later.

One hundred years after his death, a commemorative tablet was placed and unveiled in St. Mary's, Bromfield, where he had been baptised. Eric Gill, the sculptor, typographer, wood engraver, calligrapher and writer, engraved the tablet. Gill's expertise at lettering in stone was well known from the many examples of his work dedicated to those who fell during the First World War. A more suitable artist would have been difficult to find.

Many questions about Hickman, and about the influences which shaped his ideas remain unanswered. As he himself said, perhaps 'someone or other will be more fortunate' in resolving them 'beyond a possibility of doubt'.

References

1. Thomas K.B. Ether used to produce insensibility in 1821. *Brit. J. Anaesth.* 1962; **39**: 588.
2. Dudley T. Letter *Lancet* Feb 6; **i**: 163. Letter *Lancet* Mar. 27; **i**: 345. Letter *Medical Times* Sept. 4; **xvi**: 561 1847: in MS 7625; Wellcome Institute for History of Medicine.
3. Souvenir: *Henry Hill Hickman Centenary Exhibition 1830-1930.* London: Wellcome Foundation Ltd 1930.
4. Thompson C.J.S. Henry Hill Hickman: a forgotten pioneer in anaesthesia. *Brit. Med. J.* 1912; **i**: 843.
5. Pernick M.S. *A Calculus of Suffering: Pain, Professionalism, and Anesthesia in nineteenth century America.* New York: Columbia University Press 1985.
6. Leake C.D. Waters R.M. The anesthetic properties of carbon dioxide. *J. Pharm. Exp. Therap.* 1928; **33**: 280.

CHAPTER TWO

Family, Names and Influences

T homas Wright's *History and Antiquities of Ludlow*, (1826)[1], described the village of Bromfield as:

two miles from Ludlow in the vicinity and partaking of the rural elegance of Oakley Park...the noble seat of the Hon. Robert Henry Clive MP.

Hickman was baptised 'Henry Hickman' in Bromfield Parish Church *(inside back cover)* and was the seventh of thirteen children.

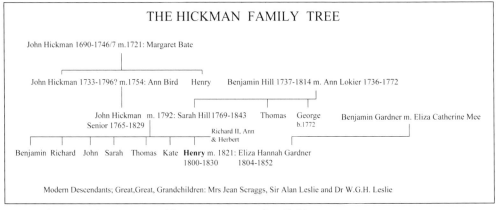

THE HICKMAN FAMILY TREE

John Hickman 1690-1746/7 m.1721: Margaret Bate

John Hickman 1733-1796? m.1754: Ann Bird   Henry   Benjamin Hill 1737-1814 m. Ann Lokier 1736-1772

John Hickman m. 1792: Sarah Hill 1769-1843   Thomas   George   Benjamin Gardner m. Eliza Catherine Mee
Senior 1765-1829   b.1772
                              Richard II, Ann
                              & Herbert

Benjamin Richard John Sarah Thomas Kate **Henry** m. 1821: Eliza Hannah Gardner
                                        1800-1830   1804-1852

Modern Descendants; Great,Great, Grandchildren: Mrs Jean Scraggs, Sir Alan Leslie and Dr W.G.H. Leslie

Fig 2. Hickman Family Tree. *Devised by Drs Armitage and Padfield.*

Hickman ancestors and siblings

Henry's father, John Hickman Sen. (1765-1829) of Lady Halton, was the youngest of four boys and two girls and he also was baptised in Bromfield. In the neighbouring parish of Culmington, on 27th March 1792, at the age of 27 years, he married Sarah (1769-1843) daughter of Benjamin Hill of the adjacent parish of Stanton Lacy. John Hickman Sen. rented the 318 acre Lady Halton farm from 1795 until his death. John and Sarah's first child, Benjamin (1792-1834), was baptised in Stanton Lacy on 22nd April 1792. That their marriage took place in Culmington, rather than in Stanton Lacy, probably related to the advanced state of Sarah's pregnancy. It is noteworthy that their first born was evidently named after Sarah's father, for no other Benjamin has been found in Hickman's pedigree and, indeed, up to that time the *International Genealogical Index* records no other Benjamin Hickman in Shropshire. Moreover, all previous eldest sons in the Hickman pedigree were baptised 'John'. Their next child, Richard (1793-1797), was also baptised in Stanton Lacy but all their other children were baptised in Bromfield. Of the six children born before Henry (Benjamin, Richard, John, Sarah, Thomas and Kate), Kate died in infancy and Richard died in childhood.

Henry's paternal grandfather, another John Hickman (1733-1796?), was the sixth child of four boys and four girls. The seventh child of that family was the only other Henry in the Hickman pedigree and he died in infancy. John Hickman (1733-1796), our Henry Hickman's grandfather, married Ann, daughter of Thomas Bird, at Stoke St. Milborough in 1754. His parents, John Hickman (1690-1746/7) and Margaret (née Bate), were married at Chirbury in 1721.

The Hill family

Hickman's mother, Sarah (1769-1843), was the sixth child of the four boys and four girls of Benjamin Hill (1737-1814) and his wife Ann (née Lokier). Ann died following the birth of her son, George, in 1772, when she was 36 and Sarah (Henry's mother-to-be) was two-and-a-half-years-old. It is not known who brought up the family. Benjamin Hill died in 1814 aged 77, but extensive search has failed to identify his baptism. In his marriage bond he was described as 'yeoman' and in his Will as 'Gentleman'. The memorial inscriptions of Benjamin Hill, his wife Ann and their second son, Thomas, are placed on the aisle floor, very close to the transept, in Stanton Lacy Parish Church. When and why they were so placed is not known, but the locations of the three memorial inscriptions seem to imply that for some reason these members of the family had the respect of the local community. Benjamin Hill lived to see the birth of all his grandchildren by Sarah. When he died in 1814, Henry Hickman was 14-years-old and probably already thinking about his future apprenticeship.

Training, qualification and marriage

Henry Hickman's schooling, the reasons for his embarking upon a medical career, the duration and circumstances of his apprenticeship and his hospital experience are unknown. He probably began his apprenticeship around 1815, the year of Napoleon's defeat and the year in which the Apothecaries Act passed through Parliament in a not very satisfactory attempt to regulate the teaching and practice of medicine[2].

In November 1819, Hickman joined the Edinburgh student body known as the Royal Medical Society, but by May 1820 he was in London where he immediately passed the diploma of Membership of the Royal College of Surgeons of England by examination. MRCS was his only formal qualification. The following year he married Eliza Hannah Gardner *(inside front cover)* of Leigh Court, near Worcester. He set up practice as a surgeon in Corve Street, Ludlow[3]. In 1822/23 there were six surgeons listed under Ludlow in *Pigot's Commercial Directory*. They were Adams and Acton in Broad Street; Foxton, John, in Broad Street; Hickman, Henry, in Corve Street; and Wakefield and Harding also in Corve Street. In addition, there were two physicians (Nicholl, Whitlock at Dinham; and Thorp, Gervase, in Broad Street), and four Druggists (Evans, Thomas, in Broad Street; Massey, William, in the Bull Ring; and Whittall and Bradford, also in the Bull Ring).

An unpriced catalogue of:

DRUGS, CHEMICAL, AND OTHER ARTICLES,
prepared and sold by
THOMAS EVANS,
Chemist and Druggist
<u>Broad Street, Ludlow</u>.

has survived in the form of a printer's proof in a scrapbook[4]. It is undated, but is proably contemporary with Hickman. In five columns it lists about five hundred items in small print. The first item is *'Aether, vitriolic & Hoffman's'*. Leeches are included. Nitre (purified) is there, but not ammonium sulphate with which it could have been reacted to get ammonium nitrate for the production of nitrous oxide. Had Hickman wanted to try nitrous oxide he would probably have had to place a special order. Heavily printed across the sheet, two thirds the way down, is:

Medicine Chests, complete,
with Directions for their Contents.

At the very bottom is printed:

A variety of Articles for Chemical and Philosophical Experiments,
MEDICAL ELECTRICITY, upon moderate terms.'

Inflating instruments (used by Hickman in some of his experiments) are not mentioned.

Henry [Hill] Hickman

Whatever anyone's reason for interposing 'Hill' (or another 'H') between 'Henry' and 'Hickman', it must have been used at least as early as September 1819. This is the date of a surviving letter, written by Hickman from Edinburgh to his fiancée and signed H.H. Hickman. The family may have warmed to the distinctive triple-H initials and the expansive euphony, if not to the ostentation of the three names. The added name may have developed its own momentum. There was, however, little consistency about its use. Copies of his Shifnal prescriptions at the Wellcome Trust seem randomly to be initialled 'HH' or 'HHH'. Of 32 examples of Hickman's name found during his lifetime, in signature or in print, only 11 included the name 'Hill' or the additional 'H'. Henry Hickman was his baptismal name; it seemed to be his ultimate preference and that was the name engraved on his tombstone. Of the next generation, his two married daughters retained the 'Hill' on their marriage certificates but his unmarried son left out the 'Hill' when registering the death of his mother.

There is evidence that Hickman served his two years apprenticeship with Drs Jukes and Watson at Stourport-on-Severn, about 15 miles from Dudley. There, a contemporary chemist by the name of Henry Hickman sold 'Hickman's Effervescing Powders, The Imperial Epicurean Zest Sauce, Dimsdale's Camphorated Tooth Powder, and also L'Moubray's Furnishing Polish, Chemical Polishing Paste and Chemical Marking Ink. Perhaps as a teenager our Henry [Hill] Hickman was sensitive but ambitious, and added the 'Hill' in order to distinguish himself from this namesake.

In 1847, immediately after the 'discovery' of ether anaesthesia, Hickman's researches of some 23 years earlier and his visit to Paris were recalled at the Académie Royale de Médecine. His pamphlet was discussed in the *Medical Gazette* and in the correspondence of Thomas Dudley of Kingswinford who championed Hickman as 'the originator of the idea of producing insensibility under surgical operations'[5]. The name 'Hill', however, was not mentioned at that time, except in the Register of Correspondence[5] of the 'Direction of Public Establishments' in Paris where his name was recorded as 'Hickmann (Henri Hill)'.

The 'Hill' was not mentioned in November 1911, when an editorial in the *British Medical Journal* drew attention to the then current research on Hickman by C.J.S. Thompson[6]. Six months later, however, Thompson reintroduced 'Henry Hill Hickman' without comment[7]. In February 1930, Mr Summerhayes, vicar of Bromfield, noticed the entry of Henry Hickman's name in the Bromfield Register of Baptisms, and he gave details to Dr Cecil Hughes*, Vice President of the Section of Anaesthetics, Royal Society of Medicine, who responded:

> *...As regards the name. We had much discussion about the inclusion of 'Hill'. The family were very concerned that it should be included, and in view of this, and of the fact, which I have verified, that he was registered at the R. Coll. of Surgeons as HHH, the Committee agreed to its inclusion. It may not coincide with the Baptism record but I take it that there can be no objection to its being on the memorial tablet...*[8].

Since that time most authors have retained the 'Hill', probably unaware of the background. The arguments favouring its retention are that the inclusion of 'Hill' must originally have had some significance, but how special is not known; that, for reasons unknown, some descendants wanted to keep it; and it may be argued by some that its modern usage confers validity. The arguments against its retention are that Hickman's name was recorded as 'Henry Hickman' at baptism and on his tombstone; that ultimately Hickman himself probably liked to do without the 'Hill'; and that it is not known why it was introduced in the first place.

Society and politics in Hickman's time.

According to Thomas Wright[1]:

> <u>Downton Castle</u>, *the property of T.A. Knight Esq., was erected under the direction of the late highly accomplished brother of its present possessor.*

That *highly accomplished brother* was Richard Payne Knight (1751-1824) who inherited a fortune accumulated by his ironmaster grandfather, Richard Knight. Richard Payne Knight (the eldest grandson) became a classical scholar, antiquarian, Member of Parliament and a trustee of the British Museum to which he left a major collection. In 1808 he gave Downton Castle to his brother, Thomas Andrew. Richard Payne Knight died on 23rd April 1824.

<u>Thomas Andrew Knight FRS (1759-1838)</u>[9]

The son of a clergyman, T.A. Knight was educated at Ludlow, Chiswick and Balliol, and he is a central figure in the Hickman story. Around 1786 he began experimenting with the grafting of fruit trees and his research soon broadened into diverse aspects of horticulture and agriculture. In 1791, he married, moved to Elton and farmed near Hereford. He was said to be indulgent and patient in conversing with the ignorant and dull, but he was also a painfully shy man. He visited Paris with his brother in 1790, but because of the French Revolution they soon returned. Knight never went back. He did little scientific reading but he did make his own apparatus. He made no contact with other scientists until meeting Sir Joseph Banks, President of the Royal Society, in 1795. Only then did he begin to realize that some of his findings were new. Over many years Banks drew him out in correspondence.

---

* *Dr Cecil Hughes had been Honorary Secretary of the Section of Anaesthetics from 1913-15 and President 1927/28. So he would have known about the Wellcome Institute interest in Hickman and by the Rev. Joyce. As Vice President 1928-31 he was perhaps the most knowledgeable of anaesthetists to carry forward the preparations for the Centenary.*

In 1797, Knight helped set up an Agricultural Society in Herefordshire and according to MacDonald[10]:

> Few names among the early Hereford breeders is [sic] more honoured than that of Thomas Andrew Knight of Downton Castle... it was he who originated a distinct variety of the Hereford cattle known as "The Knight Greys".

In plant physiology he demonstrated the effect of the force of gravity upon root growth. By 1805 his Merino-Ryland crossbred sheep were winning all the prizes at the Hereford Agricultural Society Meeting (Sir Joseph Banks had negotiated for him a Merino ram from the Royal herd). He was a member of twenty-one different scientific societies and was awarded medals by eleven of them. He was elected Fellow of the Royal Society in 1803 and was awarded its Copley Medal for his papers on vegetable physiology. In the spring of that year Sir Joseph Banks introduced him to Humphry Davy who visited him at Elton in the summer, and a long friendship began between them. Soon after moving to Downton Castle, Knight was elected President of the Royal Horticultural Society which office he held for twenty-seven years.

Napoleonic Wars and After

Throughout Hickman's life, England faced unprecedented economic and social problems, in part caused and in part accentuated by the Napoleonic Wars and their aftermath. It was a period of unrest and change and, for many, of poverty and distress. Three months before Hickman was born there appeared in *The Times* this curious but illustrative understatement:

> Several enquiries having been made of us concerning the INCOME TAX BILL, which lately passed through Parliament, we understand that it is merely a Bill for regulating the appropriation of the monies, which arose out of it. The Bill was so unimportant that it was not printed[11].

It did in fact mark the beginning of Income Tax, introduced on the understanding that it would be withdrawn after the war, which it was, in 1816. To make good some of the loss of revenue resulting from its withdrawal, duties on a multiplicity of items were introduced and they helped to raise the cost of living and penalize the less well off. The tax on glass was increased more than five fold, which was particularly resented by apothecaries who depended upon a supply of glass bottles. Income Tax was re-introduced in the 1840s. In January 1800, three weeks before Hickman's birth, *The Times* offered suggestions for the consideration of the Public, and in particular the more opulent classes of the Community:

> for the purpose of reducing the Consumption of Bread Corn; and relieving at the same time the Labouring People, by the Substitution of other cheap, wholesome, and nourishing Food; and especially by means of Soup Establishments &c... At the present interesting crisis, when the high price of bread occasions a peculiar pressure on the labouring people, every expedient which can in any degree tend to diminish the pressure becomes an important consideration... Among the various expedients which experience has shown to be best adapted to afford substantial relief, none seems to deserve so much attention as <u>Soup Establishments</u>. These excellent institutions, which have existed in the Metropolis for more than two years, have incontestibly proved how much can be attained in economising the food of man, by the necessary preparation of meat and vegetables upon a large scale, in

all instances where a design of this nature is properly methodized, and conducted with attention and regularity[12].

Two months later *The Times* reported the example set at the Palace:

The use of flour for pastry is prohibited by the Royal Family during the present scarcity. Rice is used as a substitute[13].

The same paper provided ample evidence of social unrest, for example:

Some partial disturbances have taken place in different parts of Kent in consequence of the dearness of corn. At Westerham, the populace last week broke open a flour mill, and carried off the flour in it...

Barns and outhouses in Odiham, Hampshire, and at Chapel Grinstead in Wiltshire were set on fire and burned down. Nearer home, in May 1800, cavalry dispersed a riot at Dudley with one man killed and several badly wounded and there was a similar incident at Sedgely near Wolverhampton[14]. Standard texts remind us that wages were low and that Napoleon's blockade of Britain's corn imports contributed to a rise in the price of bread. Home grown food supplies were barely sufficient to meet the needs of the rapidly growing population and the effects of a poor harvest were immediate. With the defeat of Napoleon the price of bread remained high largely due to the 1815 Corn Law. This was introduced to protect agriculture and it forbade the import of corn so long as its price at home did not exceed eighty shillings per quarter. Manufacturers, well stocked at the end of the war, were suddenly without military orders, while Continental tariffs impeded exports. Increasing problems of wage reduction and unemployment were exacerbated by near-complete demobilization, and in industrial areas there tended to be mass unemployment.

This stressful period was punctuated by violent incidents such as the Spa Fields Meeting, (1816); the March of the Blanketeers, (1817); the Peterloo Massacre, (1819) and the Cato Street Conspiracy, (1820). Lacking a police force and with memories of the French Revolution, an apprehensive government introduced counter-measures which were in part dependent upon informers, spies and *agents provocateurs* (e.g. 1816 Game Law; 1817 Suspension of the Habeas Corpus Act and in 1819 the 'Six Acts')[15-18]. Trinder[19] identified the period of depression in the iron trade between 1815 and 1822, at its worst in 1816/17, as one of profound social crisis in Shropshire. Around 1820, and for several decades thereafter, there was also said to be overcrowding in the medical profession. The majority of the practitioners recruited into the services (about 300 per year during the later years of the Napoleonic wars) were discharged when the war was over. Medicine as a career also became more popular, and medical schools produced more than enough doctors[2]. New medical schools were founded in Bristol (1818), Manchester (1824) and Sheffield (1828) followed by Leeds in the year after Hickman's death.

Morley touched on the state of affairs in Ludlow[20]. In December 1816, some of its wealthier inhabitants met in St. Lawrence's Church *to submit their resolutions relative to the present Distress of the Country*. One hundred and sixty subscribers to the Ludlow Association for the Relief of The Poor (about three per cent of the 1821 population of Ludlow) raised £700. Individual subscriptions ranged from 2/6d to £100. Morley noted that many of the Auction Sales in and around Ludlow between 1816 and 1826 were forced sales under Deeds of Assignment, Distress for Rent, by order of the Sheriff and due to Bankruptcy. The majority concerned farmers. Six months after Hickman married, his father-in-law became bankrupt and in 1822, the landlord of the Angel Inn in Ludlow also went bankrupt. In December 1824, a few months after Hickman left Ludlow for Shifnal, the *Wolverhampton Chronicle*[21] reported that:

> *The old established and respectable banking firm of Messrs Prodgers, of Ludlow, suspended payment on Wednesday last. They drew upon the house of Marsh & Co. of Berners Street, and in the failure of that concern they experienced, as did most of the provincial banks concerned with it, a very severe run. This they withstood and the prompt manner, in which they satisfied every demand on that occasion, restored them in the public confidence. The exact cause of their being compelled to take the present painful step is not known.*

At once there appeared the following printed notice in Ludlow:

> *Several inhabitants of <u>Ludlow</u>, having taken into consideration the unfortunate circumstances of Messrs. Prodger's Bank having stopped payment, may lessen the confidence of the Public in the OLD BANK ... do hereby agree to take in payment as usual, the Notes of Messrs Coleman and Wellings.*

One hundred and eighty five names were appended. Coleman and Wellings went bankrupt early in 1826[22]. The years 1825 and 1826 were particularly bad for country banks, about eighty of them became unable to pay cash to their customers on demand and went bankrupt[23].

Fig 3.
Notice displayed in Hickman's surgery.
Courtesy of the Science Museum/Science & Society Picture Library.

Such were the times when Hickman grew up and trained to be a doctor, during which both the population of England and the provision of poor relief increased appreciably. He must surely have witnessed much poverty. We cannot say how much he was affected by it except to note the following surviving and much quoted notice which he is said to have displayed in his surgery[5] and which led Fülöp-Miller[24] to head his chapter on Hickman: 'Physician to the Poor and Needy'; while Cartwright[25] saw in the notice evidence of Hickman's kindliness. *(figure 3) This is now held in the Science Museum Store, Blythe House, Blythe Road, Hammersmith, London.*

Ludlow

Thomas Wright's *History and Antiquities of Ludlow* (1826)[1], gave an account of contemporary Ludlow and its populace, communications and visitors. The population of Ludlow in 1821 was 4,820 and there were 1,006 inhabited houses and 1,139 families. From the Crown Hotel in Broad Street, the London Royal Mail went out every morning through Worcester and Oxford and another arrived from London in the afternoon. The Chester and Hereford Royal Mail through Shrewsbury arrived every morning from Hereford and returned the same evening. The Royal Mail Coach to Bishop's Castle, Montgomery, and Welsh Pool left every evening and returned the following morning. At the Angel Inn, on the other side of Broad Street, the Aurora Post Coach stopped on its way to London through Tenbury, Worcester and Oxford.

Newspapers arrived weekly: *Eddowes' Shrewsbury Journal* on Wednesdays, *Watton's Shrewsbury Chronicle* on Fridays, *Tymb's Worcester Journal* on Thursdays and *Holl's Worcester Herald* on Saturdays.

According to Wright:

Ludlow cannot boast of any particular manufactory on a large scale, the greater part of the town being inhabited by genteel families, attracted probably by the healthy and pleasant situation of the place. Its chief trade is in Gloves, in the manufacture of which a great number of persons of both sexes are employed. Besides this there is considerable business done in the paper making, tanning, timber trade, and cabinet making ... The river Corve in its course by the bottom of Corve Street ... turns a wheel to grind bark for the tanners, and puts in motion machinery for rope, cordage, and sacking makers &c. and on the Teme are also several Corn Mills, a Paper Mill, and, at the foot of Ludford Bridge, a small establishment in which many persons are employed in manufacturing the useful articles of woolen cloths, flannels, blankets, yarn &c.

Such were the sources of Hickman's patients in the town and the surrounding country.

It was while practising in Ludlow that Hickman tried operating on animals after exposing them to carbon dioxide beneath a glass cover, or after denying them fresh air. In February 1824, he described these experiments in a preliminary personal handwritten letter to T.A. Knight of Downton Castle (Chapter 5). Later that year Hickman moved to Shifnal, about thirty-five miles from Ludlow *(figure 4, p22)*. The immediate area included Ironbridge on the River Severn (named after the world's first iron bridge, erected there in 1779) about six miles from Shifnal. The area was the focal point of the Industrial Revolution in Shropshire[19], where iron, coal and clay were mined and the bright glow from blast furnaces lit the countryside. Shifnal was also the birthplace of Dr Thomas Beddoes (1760-1808) who had advocated trial of the therapeutic properties of gases. Because of Beddoes' association with Shifnal, some authors have implied that Hickman came indirectly under his influence[25], but Beddoes was established at Bristol

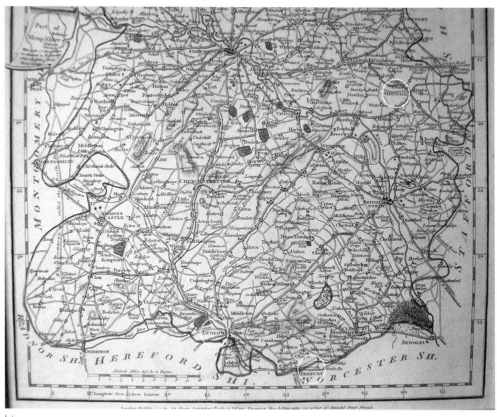

b)

Parts of Cary's Map of Shropshire, 1787.

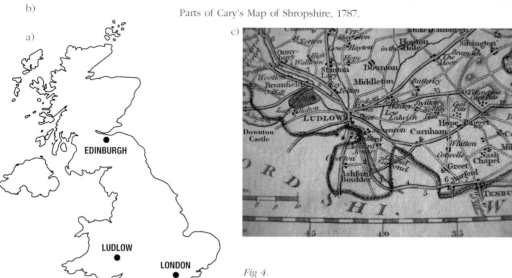

a)

EDINBURGH

LUDLOW

LONDON

c)

Fig 4.
Maps of a) the UK b) South Shropshire and c) the Ludlow area. b) Shows Ludlow, Shifnal and Tenbury and c) Lady Halton, Bromfield and Downton Castle.
Supplied by Dr A. Padfield.

by 1794 and Hickman was only eight years old when Beddoes died. Shifnal was also on the London-Holyhead road. Thomas Telford was rebuilding this road (now A5) and increased traffic was to be expected. The old road over Snedshill nearby had just been by-passed[26] and two years later the *Shrewsbury Chronicle* reported the opening of the new bridge across the Menai Strait[27].

By 1828, Hickman was listed in *Pigot & Co's Shropshire Directory* as a physician in Church Street, Shifnal[28]. Meanwhile, in August 1824, he had produced his pamphlet on *Suspended Animation...during Operations on Animals...with a view of ascertaining its probable utility in Surgical Operations on the Human Subject*, in the form of an open letter addressed to Knight, with a preface 'To The Public' (Chapter 5). This was printed at Ironbridge. Hickman doubtless hoped that his pamphlet would be discussed at the Royal Society, and that it would attract interest and support from among his medical brethren and the lay public. The Royal Society, however, has no record of Hickman or his pamphlet. Comment in the *Gentleman's Magazine* was sceptical[29] and quotation of the pamphlet in the *Shrewsbury Chronicle*[30] elicited a scathing letter to *The Lancet*[31] *(figure 7, p41)*.

There is no substantiated evidence that Hickman presented his ideas to anyone else of note in Great Britain, but in 1828 he visited Paris and appealed to Charles X, King of France, for the co-operation of His Majesty's Medical and Surgical Schools in Paris[5, 32, 33]. The Académie Royale de Médecine recorded the interest of Baron Larrey. As Napoleon's Surgeon-General, Larrey had extensive experience of war surgery under desperate circumstances. A committee was appointed to consider Hickman's appeal, but Larrey was not a member of it and the matter was not pursued[5]. Hickman returned to England and moved to another practice at 18 Teme Street, Tenbury Wells, Worcestershire, where he died in 1830. He was buried at Bromfield and 17 days later a notice of his death appeared in *Berrows Worcester Journal*:

Lately, at Tenbury, in the 31st year of his age[34].

References

1. Wright T. *The History and Antiquities of the town of Ludlow, and its ancient castle: with lives of the residents and descriptive and historical accounts of Gentlemen's Seats, villages etc.* Ludlow: Proctor and Jones 2nd ed. 1826.
2. Loudon I. *Medical Care and the General Practitioner 1750-1850.* Oxford: Clarendon Press 1986.
3. Pigot's *Commercial Directory* 1822/23.
4. Norton J. Personal communication. From private collection of early nineteenth-century proofs printed by T. Griffiths. Vol. 1 *(Held in Ludlow Museum)*.
5. Souvenir: *Henry Hill Hickman Centenary Exhibition. 1830-1930.* London: Wellcome Foundation Ltd 1930.
6. Anonymous An unfinished chapter in the history of anaesthesia. *Brit. Med. J.* 1911; **ii**: 1434.
7. Thompson C.J.S. Henry Hill Hickman. A forgotten pioneer of anaesthesia. *Brit. Med. J.* 1912; **i**: 843.
8. Ms letter from Dr Hughes to Mr Summerhayes, 15th Feb. 1930. Shropshire Record Office: 2376/5/119.
9. Bagenal N.B. Thomas Andrew Knight 1759-1838. President, Horticultural Society of London, 1811-38. *J. Roy. Horticult. Soc.* 1938; **63**: 619.
10. MacDonald J. revised by Sinclair J. *History of Hereford Cattle.* London: Vinton & Co. 1909.
11. Anonymous *The Times.* 24th October 1799.
12. Anonymous *The Times.* 2nd January 1800.
13. Anonymous *The Times.* 4th March 1800.
14. Anonymous *The Times.* 5th May 1800.
15. Hill C.P. *British Economy and Social History 1700-1982.* 5th edition London: Arnold 1985.
16. Hill C.P. and Wright J.C. *British History 1815-1914.* Oxford University Press: 1981.
17. Lowe N. *Mastering Modern British History.* London: Macmillan 1984.

18. Stern W.M. *Britain Yesterday and Today*. London: Longman 2nd ed. 1969.
19. Trinder B. *The Industrial Revolution in Shropshire*. Chichester: Phillimore 1973.
20. Morley E.L. Ludlow – after Waterloo. *Shropshire Magazine* 1964; **16**: 47.
21. Anonymous *Wolverhampton Chronicle*. 29th December 1824.
22. Bankruptcies *The Times*, 10th April 1826.
23. Valentine S. & Mason S. *Banking; Teach Yourself Books*, Hodder & Stoughton. 3rd ed. 1984.
24. Fülöp-Miller R. *Triumph Over Pain*. Translated by Eden & Cedar Paul. London: Hamish Hamilton 1938.
25. Cartwright F.F. *The English Pioneers of Anaesthesia (Beddoes, Davy and Hickman)* Bristol: John Wright & Sons 1952.
26. Trinder B. *A History of Shropshire*. Chichester: Phillimore 1983.
27. Opening of the Menai Suspension Bridge. *Shrewsbury Chronicle*, Feb. 3rd 1826.
28. Pigot and Co.; *Shropshire Directory* 1828.
29. Surgical Experiments. *Gentleman's Magazine;* Jan.-June 1825; **95**: 628.
30. Hickman H.H. On employing suspended animation during surgical operations. *Shrewsbury Chronicle*. June 3rd 1825.
31. Antiquack. Surgical Humbug. *Lancet;* 1826; **9**: 646.
32. Anonymous *Archives Générales de Médecine* Paris. 1st series 1828; **18**: 453.
33. Anonymous *Bulletin de l'Académie Royale de Médecine*. 1846-47; Tom. **XII**: 418.
34. Hickman. Obituary. *Berrows Worcester Journal*. April 22nd 1830.

CHAPTER THREE

The Search for Anaesthesia before Hickman

Interest in the deliberate alteration of consciousness to treat illness increased during the period of European Enlightenment at the end of the eighteenth- and beginning of the nineteenth-centuries. This novel therapy must have been discussed in Edinburgh, one of the most important medical schools of the era, and Hickman's alma mater.

Franz Mesmer (1734-1815) and Mesmerism

Mesmer's Viennese patients had psychosomatic problems, which were amenable to cure by his persuasive methods involving 'animal magnetism' or hypnotism. He treated various complaints, some of them bizarre. Success appeared to be associated with the occurrence of a 'crisis' in the patient, which was often signalled by convulsions. Sometimes 'cures' followed the production or worsening of pain. Occasionally the patient went into a somnambulistic trance, but rapport between patient and therapist seemed essential. Mesmer found that he could dispense with the magnets, wands and other devices which he had tried originally, and just used his hands. His treatments later developed to the point where he did not even touch his patients[1]. Mesmer had an intuitive feel for the use of suggestion and the induction of the then undefined hypnosis, and he indulged in varied degrees of self deception in forcing the marriage of clinical observations and pet theories, smothering inconsistencies with vagueness and enhancing the whole with showmanship.

A commission was set up to investigate Mesmer's cures and the case against him appeared irrefutable. In May 1777 he received a letter from the chairman expelling him from the medical faculty of Vienna and in January 1778 he moved to Paris where he again became the focus of controversy. Dr Charles d'Eslon, first physician to the Comte d'Artois (later King Charles X), gave Mesmer generous support, at some personal risk, but with limited effect. The President of the Académie des Sciences invited Mesmer to submit a memorandum on his work which he called *Mémoire sur la découverte du magnétisme animal,* but this was apparently too vague and was taken no further by the Academy.

However, the controversies were such that in 1784, a high powered French Royal Commission, including Lavoisier and Benjamin Franklin, was set up to examine 'Mesmerism'. The members paid more attention to d'Eslon and his clinic than to Mesmer and tried mesmerising each other. The outcome was that the Commission denied the existence of 'animal magnetism'. It attributed apparent cures to the imagination[2]. Goldsmith[3] noted that in some patients Mesmer saw what he called 'magnetic sleep-walking', otherwise known as 'somnambulism' or deep hypnotic trance. Patients in this state did not protest at being pinched or pricked, but Mesmer regarded these apparently anaesthetic phenomena as no more than incidental to his treatment by 'crisis'. He did not attempt to use somnambulism in order to prevent surgical or any other pain, and died near Lake Constance in 1815.

Puysegur and Deleuze

It was Mesmer's disciple, the Comte de Puysegur, who developed the use of 'somnambulism' and it became his chief therapeutic agency. Although Puysegur – with his predecessors – believed in a 'universal fluid', it no longer seemed so important and he neither touched his patients nor sought to produce 'crises'. His patients, mostly peasants, were treated in the open air beneath an old elm, which Puysegur had 'touched.' In the year of the Royal Commission one of Puysegur's patients went quietly to sleep. His physical activity seemed suspended and he responded only to the voice of the therapist, giving the impression that his mental faculties were more acute. Puysegur repeated in a quiet compelling voice that he would soon be cured – and so he was after a few treatments. During his third and fourth sessions, the patient seemed able to diagnose the seat of disease in fellow patients who confirmed his observations and were impressed. Puysegur was thus provided with a new approach in confident motivated subjects, and with excellent results[3].

The first practical book on mesmerism was written by J.F.P. Deleuze, a botanist and pupil of Puysegur. He developed the idea that the will of the 'magnetiser' was important and found that he could sometimes will his patients to behave in a particular way upon waking from a trance. In other words he introduced the concept of post-hypnotic suggestion[4].

Baron DuPotet de Sennevoy

DuPotet came from Besançon and his early interest in mesmerism culminated in the publication of his *Cours de Magnétisme en Sept Leçons* in the 1840s. He does not seem to have had a medical qualification, but he was undoubtedly accepted in Parisian medical circles. He read avidly all that he could lay hands on, but he noted the lack of a good elementary, systematic book on what we would now call hypnotism until the one published by Deleuze and referred to above. He became more deeply involved and as a medical student in 1819 wrote:

> I solicited permission to make ... experiments at the Hôtel Dieu. My request was granted, and the results published as a little brochure entitled Exposé des Expériences de l'Hôtel Dieu that was translated into German and Italian and passed through three French editions[5].

His first patient was a lady who suffered from haematemesis. During thirteen months in hospital she had resisted all treatment. Following mesmerisation – in front of thirty to forty physicians – she ceased to vomit blood. She was 'perfectly cured' in twenty-seven days. An account of the findings of a Commission of the French Academy on somnambulism was drawn up by M.M. Husson, Geoffrey, Recamier, Brichenteau and Delens. Meanwhile there were similar séances at other Paris hospitals – the Hôpital de la Pitié (M.M. Georget and Roston), the Salpêtrière (M. Esquiral) and the Hospice de la Charité (Dr Foissac)[6].

DuPotet detailed the somnambulist phenomena induced by Puysegur:

> ... jaws firmly locked; joints often rigid and inflexible; the body may be pricked and pinched, lacerated or burnt; fumes of concentrated liquid ammonia may be passed up the nostrils; the loudest reports made close upon the ear; dazzling and intense light may be thrown upon the pupil of the eye: yet so profound is the physical state of lethargy that the sleeper will remain undisturbed, and insensible to tortures which, in the waking state, would be intolerable.

Experiments without consent

DuPotet continued his account into 1820 and 1821:

Numerous experiments were performed by me in Paris, at the Hôtel Dieu and many incredulous physicians, attracted by the novelty, witnessed them and wished to satisfy themselves that there was no deception. To this I assented and according-ly they proceeded to prove the insensibility of the patients by a variety of tests, many of them cruel, but these experiments were not performed by me. It was a sort of sac-rifice of humanity which was immediately insisted upon, and in the infancy of the science I had no alternative except to permit them, or allow truth itself to be com-promised by refusal.

It is illuminating to read how those experiments were conducted; and it is also illumi-nating, yet a pity, that the thought of trying out somnambulism during surgical operations did not occur to the writer at that stage. As has been described, DuPotet's somnambulised patients were subjected to extensive study:

....their lips and nostrils were tickled with feathers; their skin was pinched until ecchymoses were produced; smoke was introduced into the nasal passages, and the feet of one woman were plunged into a strong infusion of mustard seed at high temperature. But not the slightest sign of pain did they evince. The expression of the countenance remained unchanged, nor was the pulse in any degree affected. On being awakened, however, out of the magnetic sleep, they all expressed the pain usually attendant on such applications; and were extremely angry at the treat-ment they had received.

Many of the physicians who had witnessed this scene, and who were convinced of the magnetic influence, applied to me to teach them how to conduct the operation, upon which they proceeded to convince themselves, by their own personal experi-ments, of the absolute extinction of sensibility in such cases. The means they adopted were on many occasions revolting, but the result removed every shade of doubt from their minds.

Experiments of Recamier – patients under pressure

DuPotet went on to quote from a certificate provided by Dr Robouam who was attached to the Hôtel Dieu:

On 6th January 1821, M. Recamier, on visiting the hospital, requested me to put into magnetic sleep a man named Starin.... M. Recamier first threatened him with the application of moxa [combustible material burned against the skin] if he allowed himself to fall asleep, and I caused the patient, much against his will, to pass into magnetic sleep during which M. Recamier applied the moxa to the forepart of the right thigh, which produced an eschar seventeen lines in length and eleven in breadth [a line is one tenth of an inch so these lesions measured 4.3cm x 2.75cm]. Starin did not manifest the least sign of pain, either by crying out, gesture or variation in pulse; and he did not feel the application of moxa until I had roused him out of the magnetic sleep...

He also described another experiment on 8th January 1821, on a woman named Leroy:

M. Recamier had previously threatened that he would apply the moxa if she allowed herself to fall asleep. I and Roboaum then, much against her will, caused the patient to fall into a magnetic sleep, during which M. Gilbert burned agaric

27

under her nostrils, and this nauseous smell produced no perceptible effect; then afterwards M. Recamier himself applied the moxa on the epigastric region, which produced an eschar of fifteen lines in length and nine in breadth [3.75cm x 2.25cm]; but during the operation the patient did not show the least symptoms of suffering great pain.

These two experiments place what Davison[7] described as Recamier's 'epoch-making' use of animal magnetism during cauterisation (see below), in perhaps a rather different light. After describing further similar experiments DuPotet commented (in a publication of 1838 describing experiments performed in 1821):

....From the facts above detailed, it is evident that surgical science should avail itself of this peculiar state to mitigate, or rather supersede, the necessity of inflicting pain during operations; and thus, practically applied, magnetism would be of the most essential utility[8].

Surgical operations under somnambulism
Accounts of the earliest use of somnambulism to prevent surgical pain differ. Fülöp-Miller[9] (identified Baron de Potel [sic] as one of the first to use somnambulism during surgery, followed by Recamier ('an authority on cancer') and by Cloquet ('professor of surgery'). Goldsmith[3] dated Recamier's operation as taking place in 1821 and Cloquet's in 1829. Frankau[1] also dated Recamier's operation in 1821, as did Kroger[10] noting that:

There is some evidence that M. Dubois also painlessly removed a breast under mesmeric coma in 1797, and Recamier, the French surgeon, is alleged to have performed surgery on a 'tranced' patient in 1821.

The present author (WDAS) was not able to trace Dubois, but Davison[7] made a more detailed claim on behalf of Recamier:

Joseph Claude Anselme Recamier (1774-1856), Professor of Medecine at the Collège de France, performed the first operation under intentional anaesthesia in modern times: the application of the cautery while the patient was under hypnosis. This epoch-making event appears to have been unnoticed by the historians of anaesthesia.

It must be questioned, however, whether this Recamier was the same Recamier who used moxa to test the reality of somnambulism (see above), rather than using somnambulism to prevent the pain of a therapeutic application of moxa. If these Recamiers were one and the same person, then the incident would have been more convincing as a 'first' in surgery if the moxa been surgically necessary (as distinct from just making a point); or had he immediately gone on to use somnambulism during necessary surgery?

According to Goldsmith[3] – and relating to events after Hickman's death:

In the late eighteen thirties, popular magnetisers felt themselves particularly in need of formal recognition, for they were beginning to operate on patients during the magnetic sleep ... (A) relatively trivial event brought the whole problem to the attention of the public. For some reason or other, the work of Dr Oudet, who extracted teeth while his patients were asleep, was widely discussed in Paris.

Not all the patients are likely to have regarded dental extractions as trivial! Frankau[1] also noted that:

...in 1837, Doctor Oudet of the Academy certified that he had witnessed the painless extraction of teeth under somnambulism.

Evidence of the early use of somnambulism in surgery is meagre. We have few clues as to how it came to be employed or, once trials had shown the way, why it was not followed more often. In asking why Hickman was ridiculed by the Académie Royale de Médecine we should also ask why was there not a series of painless operations by, for example, M. Cloquet?

M. Cloquet and Mme. Plantin

One example of an operation under somnambulism which was well reported is that of the mastectomy performed on Mme. Plantin by Jules Cloquet on 12th April, 1829, fourteen years after Mesmer died, seventeen years before Morton's demonstration, but during Hickman's lifetime. It was probably the first major operation under mesmerism and was reported in *The Lancet*[11], quoting from *La Clinique et La Lancette Française*. The case made apparent the possibility of surgery without pain, but we lack evidence that the potential significance of this was appreciated by other workers at the time.

M. Larrey of the Académie very much doubted that, during the operation, the patient had really been in a state of somnambulism. He declared her to be an imposter who, for the sake of money, had taken part in the trickery of the magnetisers, and who, by the force of her will, had been able to undergo the operation without evincing any sign of pain. He had seen many instances of apparent insensibility in persons who were not somnambulists, and he himself had performed the most painful operations on soldiers in the field of battle who sang the hymns of Mars, and exhorted their comrades to keep up their courage. He mentioned the incident of the fanatic murderer of Kléber at Cairo, who, under the most terrible tortures, appeared insensible. He concluded by saying that he considered it very dangerous to let the public believe it possible for a good surgeon to be the dupe of such magnetic imposters, and that he should be ashamed to see his name associated with a fact of this kind. With respect to the insensibility to pain in several persons, M. Hervé de Cheguin observed that females of nervous temperament, and pious disposition especially, frequently bore the most cruel operations with astonishing indifference.

In reply to M. Larrey, M. Cloquet said there was not the least reason to suspect the character of the patient: her rank, education, and wealth, placed her above the suspicion of assisting a fraudulent contrivance, or having been influenced by pecuniary interest. As to the instances of insensibility mentioned by M. Larrey, he had seen many cases of a similar kind, but there was a great difference between real want of sensation and *apparent* insensibility, in consequence of the will and an unusual firmness of mind. In persons gifted with the latter, he had always seen some expression of pain, though perhaps not of the common kind; singing, and an animated conversation, are generally used by them, to distract the attention as much as possible; and the complete silence of the sufferer, the state of the countenance, muscular contraction of the hands etc, always betray the real condition[12].

Hickman, Cloquet and Larrey

Two points about Cloquet's mastectomy need airing.

Firstly, the mastectomy was reported to the Académie Royale de Médecine only six months after the Academy's attention had been drawn to Hickman's petition addressed to Charles X.

Secondly, the influential Baron Larrey participated in the discussions of both Hickman's petition and Cloquet's report of the mastectomy. These factors invite a comparison of the learned society's attitude to the petition and to the operation report, which shared an interest in painless surgical operations.

Carbon dioxide as an anaesthetic before Hickman's time

As Cartwright[13] points out, we do not know who or what gave Hickman his idea of pain-less surgery, nor what led him to the means he employed – the inhalation of carbon dioxide or brief deprivation of oxygen. However, unpublished notes of lectures given at St. George's Hospital, London, by Benjamin Collins Brodie, dated January 1821, describe administration of carbonic acid (gas) to a guinea pig in a bell glass. It became insensible after two minutes, but recovered a few minutes after being removed from the bell glass. In February 1821, his notes mention the administration of ether to another guinea pig, which became insensible after four minutes and after twelve minutes appeared dead, though the heart was still beating[14]. It was given artificial respiration for about five minutes and after twenty-five minutes it had pretty well recovered. A manuscript in the Library at St. George's Hospital headed: *Experiment Feby 5 1821 Present Mr Cutler & Mr Good* describes in minimally different wording what appears to be precisely the latter experiment and written in the same hand. Few people witnessed the original experiment; only they and the audience at the lectures would have known about it at a time when opposition to animal experimentation was becoming apparent.

In the small amount of Hickman's writings available to us he acknowledged that

> ... *from the many experiments on suspended animation I have wondered that: some hint has not been thrown out of its probable utility....*

> And again.... *The facility of suspending animation by carbonic acid gas, and other means, without permanent injury to the subject, having been long known, it appears to me rather singular that no experiments have hitherto been made with the object of ascertaining whether operations could be successfully performed upon animals while in a torpid state.*

The reference to suspended animation may in part stem from Edmund Goodwyn's *The Connection of Life with Respiration* of 1788[15] in which the author describes temporary loss of consciousness – or suspended animation – brought about by drowning, hanging, or breathing carbonic acid gas or disoxygenated air. Goodwyn proposed that the terms 'suspended animation' and 'suspended life', which he had discussed at length, should be more precisely used because they suggested resuscitation of the truly dead. It is clear, therefore, that the concept of temporary suspended animation had been current for a considerable period before Hickman's lifetime and experimental work.

Interest in the possible use of carbon dioxide as an anaesthetic was revived in 1870 by a letter from Sir James Young Simpson to Dr Jacob Bigelow. Simpson pointed out that Dr Hickman suggested carbonic acid as a soporific:

> ...*in imitation of the experiments performed for ages on the poor dogs at the Grotto del Cane*[16].

The Dog's Grotto

There is no known evidence that Hickman consciously imitated experiments performed at the Grotto del Cane, but that does not necessarily mean that he did not. Dogs were certainly frequently and routinely brought near to death by immersion in the carbon dioxide lying on the floor of the grotto, and resuscitated by placing them in fresh air before the circulation of the blood had died away. The Grotto del Cane had been well described in travel literature. In 1828, for example, Simond[17] gave an account of a tour he made in Italy and Sicily a decade earlier (1817-1818). He had visited the Grotto del Cane around the time that Sir Joseph Banks was writing to Knight on cruelty to animals during experimental research, and about a year before Hickman went up to Edinburgh. The description of the Grotto was brief and to the point:

...we visited Lake Agnano, which, like all other lakes of this region of fire, was once the crater of a volcano, and on its bare and melancholy shores we found the celebrated Grotto del Cane, but declined witnessing the idle and cruel experiment usually performed on an unlucky dog doomed to exhibit his daily agonies for the amusement of the vulgar...

Rees' Universal Dictionary of 1819[18] quotes a much earlier account by Dr Mead (1673-1754)[19] who described the celebrated 'mofeta' or 'bucca venenosa' (poisonous mouth), some two miles from Naples. Mead gave its dimensions as eight feet high, twelve feet long and 6 feet broad and told how:

from the ground arises a thin subtle warm fume, visible enough to the discerning eye ... the colour of the sides of the grotto being the measure of its ascent ... for so far it is darkish green, but higher only common earth ... when ... a dog, or any other creature, is forcibly kept below (this level), or by reason of its smallness, cannot hold its head above it; it presently loses all motion, falls down as dead or in a swoon; the limbs convulsed and trembling, till at last no more signs of life appear than a very weak and almost insensible beating of the heart and arteries, which if the animal be left a little longer, quickly ceases too, and the case is irrecoverable... But if it is taken out in time, and laid in the open air, it soon comes to life again.

François Magendie (1783-1855), the great French physiologist, visited the grotto accompanied by a Dr Constantin James. Years later, in 1844, James published his *Voyage Scientifique avec M. Magendie en 1843*[20] and the following is his account of the grotto freely translated by the present author:

Dr James got down on his knees, put his head into the carbonic acid gas and held his breath for fifteen seconds after which his eyes smarted. After a few breaths of fresh air he got back on his knees and tried swallowing without breathing. The taste was agreeable. He then took a single deep breath of the gas and experienced a sort of vertiginous dizzyness and a painful tightening of the whole chest. Instinct and common sense made him lift up his head for air. After a few minutes the sensations disappeared and he proceeded with more caution. On taking a short breath of the gas the feelings of suffocation were less. After continuing the trial he felt a disagreeable sensation like champagne up his nostrils. He then put a rabbit in the grotto for seventy-five seconds after which it seemed quite dead but it began breathing again after about five minutes and seemed to have quite recovered after about fifteen. He repeated the experiment but tried a kind of artificial respiration by pressing alternately the animal's chest and abdomen and he reported that the animal revived more promptly but times were not stated. Again after seventy-five seconds' exposure he tried gentle repeated mouth-to-mouth insufflation (man to rabbit). *First signs of spontaneous respiration appeared after about twenty seconds* (compared with five minutes in the first experiment). *Repeating this experiment with two rabbits exposed for three minutes each, at the end of fifteen minutes the one given mouth-to-mouth insufflation had recovered and the one left alone had died without showing any signs of recovery.*

Similar experiments were reported by Herpin of Metz in 1858[21] and the Grotto del Cane evidently remained popular with tourists for many years. It was still being described in the eleventh edition of *Baedeker's Italy: Handbook for Travellers* in 1893[22], which added that the Lago d'Agnano had a circumference of two-and-a-quarter miles and that it was drained in 1870. The description of the grotto was little changed.

Dr James' account of the Grotto del Cane might have been fresh in Simpson's mind when he wrote his historical review of pain relief in surgery in 1847[23], but there does not appear to be any record of his having drawn attention to this grotto before his letter to Bigelow in 1870. Dr James did not visit the Grotto del Cane until thirteen years after Hickman's death but similar earlier accounts, such as that of Addison of the first decade of the eighteenth-century[24] could well have had an influence on Hickman's work.

References

1. Frankau G. Introductory Monograph in: *Mesmerism by Dr. Mesmer (1779) being the first translation of Mesmer's historic Mémoire sur la Découverte du Magnétisme Animal to appear in English*. London: Macdonald 1948.
2. Animal Magnetism [Book Review] Report of the Experiments on Animal Magnetism… by J.C. Colquhoun. *Lancet;* 1833; **23**: 175-183 and 205-218.
3. Goldsmith M. *Franz Anton Mesmer: the History of an Idea*. London: Barton 1934.
4. Deleuze J.P.F. *A History of Animal Magnetism in two parts*. 1816 Translated from the French.
5. DuPotet de Sennevoy D.J. Baron. *Expériences publiques sur le magnétisme animal faites à l'hôtel Dieu de Paris;* 2me ed. augmentée des dernières délibérations de l'Académie de Médecine du..... mémoire de M. Loissac du rapport fait par M.Husson 1826.
6. Animal Magnetism. *Lancet;* 1831; 20: 573.
7. Davison M.H.A. *The Evolution of Anaesthesia*. Altrincham: John Sherratt and Son 1965.
8. DuPotet de Sonnervoy J.D. Baron. *An Introduction to the study of Animal Magnetism with an appendix containing reports of British Practitioners in favour of the Science*. London: Saunders 1838.
9. Fülöp-Miller R. *Triumph over Pain*. Translated by Eden & Cedar Paul. London: Hamish Hamilton 1938.
10. Kroger W.S. *Introduction to Hypnosis in Medicine and Surgery* originally titled *Mesmerism in India. The work of James Esdaile*. New York: Institute for Research in Hypnosis Publication Society and The Julian Press 1957.
11. Animal Magnetism. *Lancet;* 1829; **16**: 293.
12. Animal Magnetism. *Lancet;* 1829; **16**: 198-199.
13. Cartwright F.F. *The English Pioneers of Anaesthesia (Beddoes, Davy, and Hickman)*. Bristol: John Wright & Sons Ltd 1952.
14. Thomas K.B. Ether used to produce insensibility in 1821. *Brit. J. Anaesth.*; 1962; **34**: 588-9.
15. Goodwyn E. *The Connexion of Life with Respiration, or an Experimental Inquiry into the effects of Submersion, Strangulation and Several Kinds of Noxious Airs on Living Animals: with an Account of the Nature of the Disease they produce, its Distinction from Death itself, and the most Efficient Means of Cure*. London; J. Johnson 1788.
16. Simpson J.Y. *Works* Vol 2. Edinburgh: A. & C. Black 1871.
17. Simond L. *A tour in Italy and Sicily*. London: Longman, Rees, Orme, Browne & Green 1828.
18. Rees A. *The Cyclopaedia or Universal Directory of Arts Sciences and Literature* Vol. 17. London: Longman, Hunt, Rees, Orme and Brown 1819.
19. Mead R. *A mechanical account of poisons in several essays: Essay VI, of venemous exhalations from the earth, poisonous air and waters*. 4th Edition. London: Brindley 1747.
20. James C. *Voyage Scientifique avec M. Magendie en 1843*. Paris: Dusillon 1844.
21. Herpin M. J. Ch. Note sur l'emploi du gaz carbonique comme agent anesthésique. *Comptes Rendus Acad Sci.*; 1858; **46**: 581.
22. Baedeker. *Italy. Handbook for Travellers. Third Part Southern Italy and Sicily,* 11th ed. 1893.
23. Simpson J.Y. Historical research regarding the superinduction of insensibility to pain in surgical operations; and an announcement of a new anaesthetic agent. *Month. J. Med. Sci.*; 1847; **8**: 451.
24. Addison J. *Remarks on several parts of Italy in the years 1701, 1702, 1703*. London: Tonson 1705.

CHAPTER FOUR

The Medical Background
to Hickman's Work

At the Wellcome celebration of Hickman in 1930 Lord Dawson of Penn pointed out that 'Hickman came from West Country stock, like his contemporary Jenner and was, like Jenner, a general practitioner'[1]. Hickman, however, was the son of a farmer; Jenner the son of a clergyman. Unlike Hickman, who appears to have had a truncated medical education, Jenner extended his training by two years as house-pupil to the famous anatomist, physiologist, pathologist, comparative zoologist and surgeon of St. George's Hospital, London, John Hunter (1728-1793). Hunter and Jenner became great friends and they corresponded regularly. In 1789, with Hunter's support, Jenner was elected a Fellow of the Royal Society following his detailed description of the known, but difficult to observe, behaviour of newly hatched cuckoos.

Hickman left no evidence of any eminent friends in London, although his correspondent T.A. Knight Esq. FRS, of Downton Castle, near Ludlow, was a friend of Sir Joseph Banks and Sir Humphry Davy, both of whom became Presidents of the Royal Society. Hickman had his own museum of natural history in Ludlow, but we do not know its origin or its extent. Although he was born after John Hunter died, he may have been inspired by Hunter's reputation or by his museum in the Royal College of Surgeons in London. Other museums, however, were being set up at the beginning of the nineteenthth-century and at least part of Hickman's museum was auctioned with other contents of his house when he moved from Ludlow to Shifnal. *(figure 5: Auction Notice)*.

Edward Jenner (1749-1823) and Henry Hickman (1800-1830)

Jenner got the seed of an idea of great potential during his apprenticeship, when a milk-maid told him:

> *I cannot take the smallpox for I have had cowpox.*

This seed germinated over many years of clinical observation, inquiry and discussion until, in 1796, he carried out the crucial experiment which confirmed the milkmaid's belief and pointed the way towards the introduction of vaccination. However, at the time of Jenner's first public announcement of vaccination in 1798, and for many years subsequently, the proposal of inoculating with vaccinia for the prevention of smallpox was met by members of the medical profession with incredulity, ridicule and direct and determined opposition.

The crucial part of Jenner's research into the immunity conferred by the cowpox against infection by smallpox was carried out between Hunter's death and Hickman's birth and his *Inquiry into the Causes and Effects of the Variolae Vaccinae, a Disease discovered in some of the Western Counties of England, particularly Gloucestershire and known by the name The Cow Pox* was published in 1798.

LUDLOW.

The Public are respectfully informed that the valuable Modern Furniture, Bedding, &c.
with a very curious Collection of

STUFFED BIRDS & ANIMALS,

The Property of Mr. HENRY HICKMAN, (who is leaving LUDLOW,) will be submitted to

PUBLIC

AUCTION,

AT HIS RESIDENCE IN CORVE STREET,

BY J. BACH,

On Monday, Tuesday, and Wednesday, the 24th 25th and 26th days of May, 1824.

THE

FURNITURE,

(NEW WITHIN A SHORT TIME,)

Is of Choice Wood and elegant designs, and comprises Mahogany and Rose-wood
Dining and Drawing-room Tables, Chairs, Secretaire and Book-case, Elegant Side-
board on Carved Pillars, ditto Sofa with Grey Moreen and Chintz Covers and Win-
dow Curtains to Match, hung on Gilt Pole, with French Rings, Scarlet Printed
ditto on Green Pole, Rose-wood Teapoy neatly fitted, Chimney Glass with Gilt
Plaster Frames, Brussels and other Carpets and Hearth Rugs, Handsome Fenders
on Brass Mountings and Claw Feet, Sliding Fire Irons, &c. &c.

The Up-stairs Furniture is very superior, Beds of fine Goose Feathers, upon lofty carved 4-Post Bedsteads, with
Fawn Moreen Furniture, handsome Ornamented Canopy top, full trimmed with Ball Fringe; Tent, Bureau, and
other Bedsteads and Hangings, Mattresses, Dressing Tables, Cane painted inclosed Dressing Cases, Pier and Swing
Glasses, Mahogany Wardrobe with Sliding Trays, pair of three height Mahogany Bedsteps completely fitted,
new Oak Chest with Drawers, 8-day Clock in new Oak Case, Hall Chairs, and Hat Stand, and a general assortment
of Kitchen Requisites, Brewing Utensils and Casks.

The Rare Collection of Stuffed

BIRDS & ANIMALS,

Including nearly TWO HUNDRED different Subjects, will afford a high Treat to Connoisseurs having been pronounced Master Pieces
in the Art.

Catalogues will be published four days previous to the Sale, and may be had at the Printers Ludlow, the Principal Inns, and of the Auctioneer,
and the whole may be Viewed three days previous to the Sale.

N. B. All Persons who have any demand against Mr. HENRY HICKMAN, are desired to send their Accounts to Messrs. ADAMS AND ANDERSON,
Solicitors, Ludlow, that the be examined and discharged, and all Persons who are indebted are requested to pay the same immediately to the said Messrs. ADAMS AND ANDERSON, who are authorised to receive the same.

April 28, 1824.---T. Griffiths, Printer, Bull-Ring, Ludlow.

Fig 5. Auction Sale Notice, detailing furniture, &c. and collection of stuffed animals.
Courtesy of Ludlow Museum Resource Centre.

Jenner's dedication to George III
Jenner dedicated the second edition of his book to the King.

Sir,

When I first addressed the public on a Physiological subject, which I conceived to be of the utmost importance to the future welfare of the human race, I could not presume in that early stage of the investigation to lay the result of my Inquiries at your Majesty's feet.

Subsequent experiments instituted not only by myself, but by men of the first rank in the medical profession, have now confirmed the truth of the theory which I first made known to the world.

Highly honoured by the permission to dedicate the result of my Inquiries to your Majesty, I am enabled to solicit your gracious patronage of a discovery which reason fully authorizes me to suppose will prove peculiarly beneficial to the preservation of the lives of mankind.

To a Monarch no less than emphatically styled the Father of his People, this Treatise is inscribed with perfect propriety; for, conspicuous as your Majesty's patronage has been of Arts, of Sciences, and of Commerce, yet the most distinguished feature of your character is your paternal care for the dearest interests of humanity.

I am, sir,

With the most profound respect,
Your Majesty's most devoted
Subject and Servant
Edward Jenner.

Jenner may never have heard of Hickman, but Hickman surely had heard of Jenner. Early in his brief career, Hickman also had an idea of great potential: to prevent suffering during surgery by introducing certain gases into the lungs. We do not know how the idea first formed in his mind, but we do know that he put it to the test of animal experiment and that he sought patronage and collaboration. When he published his findings he too was ridiculed and accused of quackery. He did not live to see his idea applied to human surgical sufferers.

Hickman's petition to Charles X of France
Although there is no evidence to suggest that Hickman modelled his petition to Charles X (Appendix A) upon Jenner's dedication of his book to George III, it could have supported fantasies about his future role in society if he had done so. There are certainly passages in Hickman's petition which imply an awareness of the potential importance of his project to mankind, for example

In addressing Your Majesty upon a subject of great importance to mankind... confidence in Your Majesty's disposition to countenance valuable discoveries... agonising, dangerous and delicate surgical operations may be performed, with perfect safety, and exemption from pain, on brute animals... the same salutory effects may be produced on the human frame...

...I have discovered a number of facts connected with this important subject; and I wish to bestow them on society.

...our species rise in the scale of moral and intellectual greatness, in proportion as our efforts are directed to the diminution of the sum of human misery, and physical evil...

Jenner's dedication of his book to George III contains the passage *...by men of the first rank in the medical profession...* which may be compared with the passage in Hickman's pamphlet *...the particular request of gentlemen of the first rate talent who rank high in the scientific world...* but any similarity between these two quotations most probably does no more than reflect English usage of the time. We may note, however, that Hickman also expressed his desire.

> *at a fit opportunity, to solicit the honour of presenting to Your Majesty, in person... a Book containing an account of my discovery which, as far as I know or can learn, has entirely originated with myself...*

This book has never been found, but should it materialize, we would doubtless find it dedicated to Charles X.

A translation of Laennec's book on chest disease

Auscultation for the diagnosis of chest disease was introduced as Hickman qualified. The work of the French physician, Laennec, on the use of his invention – the stethoscope – was translated into English, and first appeared in 1821 with a second, much improved edition in 1827[2,3]. The *London Medical Repository's* reviewer of the first edition ventured to predict that Laennec's work *will become a favourite with the British pathologist.*

The reviewer of the second edition elaborated:

> *The chief value, and that is great, of the work of M. Laennec, consists in the minute and accurate description of the anatomical characters of the disease which it comprehends, and of those signs which he has found, during a very extensive and persevering practise, to be pathognomonic of each disease. That he has given rise to a new era of the mode of exploring the functions of the thoracic viscera, both in health and disease, must be fully admitted, as a great tribute to his memory...*

The second review was published in January 1828, three months before Hickman arrived in Paris (Chapter 6). He could have seen it before leaving Shifnal, and in favour of Hickman having been a reader of the *London Medical Repository* is the fact that it published a contribution by him in September 1821[4]. Laennec died in 1826, but demonstration of his methods by Parisian colleagues could have become an additional attraction for Hickman's visit, especially as by then he called himself a physician. Indeed this might help to explain the following wording of his petition to the King of France:

> *Permit me, Sire, to state that I am a British Physician, Member of the Royal College of Surgeons, London, ...*

However, McMenemey revealed that Charles Hastings (later founder of the British Medical Association) was not familiar with the value of percussion and auscultation in his early days as a physician at the Worcester Infirmary, in the 1820s[4], so we should not assume that Hickman knew of these innovations. But percussion and auscultation aside, this was a period when many English doctors attended the hospitals in Paris.

References

1. Dawson of Penn, Lord. Speech. *The Times;* p15; April 5th 1930.
2. Laennec R.T.H. *De l'Auscultation Médiate du Traité du Diagnostique des Malades.* Paris, Drosson 1819, 1826, 1831.
3. Ibid, translated into English by John Forbes 1821.
4. Hickman H.H. Abscess of the Spleen communicating with the Stomach and Umbilicus. *London Medical Repository;* September 1821; **16**; 202.
5. McMenemey W.H. *A History of the Worcester Infirmary.* London 1947.

CHAPTER FIVE

Correspondence and Experiments

Hickman's ideas and experimental work are best explained in his own words. His first letter was addressed to T.A. Knight Esq., of Downton Castle, Herefordshire, the man he hoped would become his sponsor. It is reproduced here by courtesy of The Wellcome Trustees. Handwritten and dated 21st February 1824, it reads as follows:

Dear Sir,

The object of the operating surgeon is generally considered to be the relief of his patient by cutting some portion of the body whereby parts are severed from each other altogether or relieving cavities of the aggravating cause of the disease*. There is not an individual who does not shudder at the idea of an operation, however skilful the surgeon or urgent the case, knowing the great pain that the patient must endure, and I have frequently lamented, when performing my own duties as a surgeon that something has not been thought of whereby the fears may be tranquillised and suffering relieved. Above all, from the many experiments on suspended animation I have wondered that some hint has not been thrown out, of its probable utility, and noticed by surgeons, and consequently I have been induced to make experiments on animals, endeavouring to ascertain the practicability of such treatment on the human subject, and by particular attention to each individual experiment I have witnessed results which show that it may be applied to the animal world and ultimately I think will be found used with perfect safety and success in surgical operations.

Fig 6. Downton Castle in 1944. *Supplied by Dr Adrian Kuipers.*

I have never known of a case of a person dying after inhaling Carbonic Acid Gas, if proper means were taken to restore the animal powers, and I have no hesitation in saying that suspended animation may be continued a sufficient time for any surgical operation providing the surgeon acts with skill and promptitude; and I think it would be found particularly advisable in cases where haemorrhage would be dangerous or the Surgeon is apprehensive of gangrene taking place after the operation, as it is well known that carbon has a most powerful antiputrescent quality. It will be found, if the means for suspending animation are slow and gradual, the return [of the powers] of life will be in the same proportion; if the means of suspension are sudden, it generally happens by the application of certain agents that the return of life is equally so; and I think it very probable if the Galvanic Fluid could have been applied in cases that proved fatal the persons may have been saved. From a number of others I have selected the experiments now sent, each is correctly noted in as few words as possible and which I think will prove a vast object.

   With great respect I am Dr Sir Your Obt. St.

                           (signed) H.H.Hickman.

                               Ludlow, Feby. 21st, 1824

T.A.Knight, Esqr.

* This form of wording for describing the object of the operating surgeon was also used in his pamphlet (see later), but the original version in the pre-amended manuscript was preferable:

> *...whereby parts are severed from each other altogether or cavities relieved of the aggravating cause of disease.*

Commentary on the handwritten letter

The abruptness of the opening sentence, launching directly into the duties of the operating surgeon, suggests that this letter may not have been the first communication on the subject between Hickman and Knight. Perhaps Hickman was granted a preliminary interview at which he was asked to put his ideas in writing. The manuscript shows that there was a slight hold-up in writing the opening sentence. At first he wrote 'or cavities relieved,' then he deleted 'relieved' and inserted 'relieving' before 'cavities', and in the end he still did not get it quite right. The phrase 'operating surgeon' immediately reminds us that there was more to surgery than operating. As Loudon[1] has pointed out, most surgery at that time consisted of dealing with relatively minor conditions, sometimes treated manually, but more often by medical measures.

    Hickman lamented the lack of means to tranquillize the fear and to relieve the suffering due to surgical operations. He wondered whether some hint had been thrown out by 'the many experiments on suspended animation.' Questions arise. To what experiments did he refer? What was understood by and about suspended animation at that time? Was he aware of Brodie's experiments referred to in Chapter 3? Hickman experimented with animals successfully and anticipated ultimate success during surgical operations in humans, making the point that he had never known a case of a person dying after inhaling carbonic acid gas if proper means were taken to restore the animal powers. What first- or second-hand experience could Hickman have had of patients inhaling and recovering from carbonic acid gas? What did Hickman regard as proper means for restoring animal powers? It seems implicit that Hickman also knew instances where proper means were not applied and patients died, implying a recognized risk. Can these be identified? Was he referring to the Dog's Grotto?

Hickman expressed confidence in the possibility of suspended animation being continued long enough for any surgical operation, provided the surgeon was prompt and skilful. One might, therefore, expect Hickman to give serious thought to the duration of surgery. He recommended his method where haemorrhage would be dangerous although he did not explain its advantage under these circumstances. Because of the supposed antiputrescent property of carbon he also recommended the inhalation of carbonic acid gas where postoperative gangrene was feared. He maintained that if the means of suspending animation were slow and gradual, the return of the powers of life would correspond. In his penultimate sentence he said he thought it 'very probable, if the Galvanic Fluid could have been applied in cases that have proved fatal, the persons may have been saved' and he ended the letter:

> From a number of others I have selected the experiments now sent; each is correctly noted in as few words as possible, which I think will prove a vast object.

There seems to be an emphasis in the letter above on 'as few words as possible'. This may reflect his own ideas or he may have been acting on advice received from someone else. Hickman stated his case but asked no favours, although we do not know what additional verbal exchanges there had been between him and Knight.

In this letter of February 1824 to Knight, Hickman gave an account of his experiments up to that date:

Experiment 1st.

20th March. [1823?]

I took a puppy a month old and placed it on a piece of wood surrounded by water over which I put a glass cover so as to prevent access of atmospheric air; in ten minutes he showed great marks of uneasiness, in twelve respiration became difficult, and in seventeen minutes ceased altogether; at eighteen minutes I took off one of the ears, which was not followed by haemorrhage; respiration soon returned and the animal did not appear to be the least sensible to pain; in three days the ear was perfectly healed.

2nd.

Four days after the same puppy was exposed to a decomposition of the carbonate of lime by sulphuric acid. In one minute respiration ceased; I cut off the other ear which was followed by a very trifling haemorrhage, and as before, did not appear to suffer any pain; in four days the wound healed. The day after operation he seemed to require an additional quantity of food, which induced me to weigh him, and I found he gained nine oz. 1 drachm and 24 grains in nine days.

3rd. 6th April.

I took the same puppy and proceeded as in experiment 1 and respiration was acted on in much the same manner. I cut off the tail, and made an incision over the muscles of the loins through which I passed a ligature and made it tight. No appearance of uneasiness until the following day, when inflammation came on and subsequent suppuration. The ligature came away in the seventh day, and wound healed on twelfth, and the dog is remarkably increased in size and now perfectly well.

Exp. 4th.

A mouse was confined under a glass surrounded by water; by means of a small tube a foot long I passed carbonic acid gas very slowly prepared into the glass; respiration

39

ceased in three minutes. I cut all its legs off at the first joint and plunged it into a basin of cold water; the animal immediately recovered and ran about the table apparently without pain; the stumps soon healed, and I kept it a fortnight, after which I gave it liberty.

Exp. 5th.

I took an adult dog and exposed him to carbonic acid gas quickly prepared and in large quantity. Life appeared to be extinct in about twelve seconds. Animation was suspended for 17 minutes, allowing respiration occasionally to intervene by the application of inflating instruments. I amputated a leg without the slightest appearance of pain to the animal. There was no haemorrhage from the smaller vessels. The ligature that secured the main artery came away on the fourth day, and the dog recovered without expressing any material uneasiness.

Exp. 6th.

I exposed a rabbit to the same gas as Exp. 5th, and cut off both ears and I experienced a similar result.

Exp. 7th.

I filled a glass globe with the gas exhaled from my own lungs; into it I put a kitten. In twenty seconds I took off its ears and tail; there was very little haemorrhage, and no appearance of pain in the animal.

The Pamphlet of 14th August, 1824

Before considering in detail these experiments included with Hickman's letter of 21st February, let us look at the text of his printed pamphlet of 14th August. The title of the pamphlet was fifty-eight words long. The text comprised an introductory section of about four hundred words headed 'TO THE PUBLIC', and 'A LETTER, &c.' in two parts, of nearly three hundred and five hundred words each, between which were placed his descriptions of a number of experiments. The texts of the pamphlet and the letter are given below. The repeated or extended experimental data he gave on this occasion differ to some extent from the earlier accounts. *(figure 7: Title page of Pamphlet, p41)*

Note: AND READ TO IT BY SIR HUMPHRY DAVY is deleted therein.

TO THE PUBLIC At the particular request of gentlemen of the first rate talent, and who rank high in the scientific world, it is, that the author of the following letter is induced to lay it before the public generally, but more particularly his medical brethren; in the hope that some one or other, may be more fortunate in reducing the object of it beyond a possibility of doubt. It may be said, and with truth, that publications are too frequently the vehicles of self-adulation, and as such, suffer greatly from the lash of severe criticism; but the author begs to assure his readers, that his views are totally different, merely considering it a duty incumbent on him (as a medical practitioner, and servant to the public), to make known any thing which has not been tried, and which ultimately may add something towards the relief of human suffering, arising from acute disease. The only method of obtaining this end is, in the author's opinion, candid discussion, and liberality of sentiment, which, too commonly is a deficient ingredient in the welfare of so important a profession, productive of serious consequences, not only for the parties themselves, but to the patient whose life is entrusted to their care. The duty and object, however, of the Physician and Surgeon, is generally considered to be the relief of a fellow creature, by applying certain remedies to the cure of internal affections,

A

LETTER

ON

SUSPENDED ANIMATION,

CONTAINING

EXPERIMENTS

Shewing that it may be safely employed during

OPERATIONS ON ANIMALS,

With the View of ascertaining

ITS PROBABLE UTILITY IN SURGICAL OPERATIONS ON THE

𝕳𝖚𝖒𝖆𝖓 𝕾𝖚𝖇𝖏𝖊𝖈𝖙,

Addressed to

T. A. KNIGHT, ESQ. OF DOWNTON CASTLE,
Herefordshire,

ONE OF THE PRESIDENTS OF THE ROYAL SOCIETY,

▓▓▓ ▓▓▓ ▓▓▓▓▓ ▓▓ ▓▓ ▓▓ ▓▓▓▓▓▓ ▓▓▓▓

———

BY DR. H. HICKMAN,
OF SHIFFNAL ;

Member of the Royal Medical Societies of Edinburgh, and of
the Royal College of Surgeons, London.

———

IRONBRIDGE : Printed at the Office of W. Smith.
1824.

Fig 7. Title Page of 1824 Pamphlet with line deleted above 'Dr. H. Hickman'.
Courtesy of the Wellcome Trust Medical Photographic Library.

or cutting some portion of the body, whereby parts are severed from each other altogether, or relieving cavities of the aggravating cause of disease. There is not an individual, he believes, who does not shudder at the idea of an operation, however skilful the Surgeon, or urgent the case, knowing the great pain that must necessarily be endured; and it is frequently lamented by the operator himself, that something has not been done to tranquillise fear, and diminish the agony of the patient. With this view of the subject then, it is, that he submits his observations and experiments to the public in the brief form of a letter to a private gentleman of the highest talent as a man of science, who with others, thought them worthy to be laid before the Royal Society; and if one grain of knowledge can be added to the general fund, to obtain a means for the relief of pain, the labours of the author will be amply rewarded.

A LETTER, &c.

Sir,

The facility of suspending animation, by carbonic acid gas, and other means, without permanent injury to the subject, having been long known, it appears to me rather singular that no experiments have hitherto been made with the object of ascertaining whether operations could be successfully performed on animals whilst in a torpid state; and whether wounds inflicted upon them in such a state would be found to heal with greater or less facility than similar wounds inflicted on the same animals whilst in possession of all their powers of feeling and suffering. Several circumstances led me to suspect that wounds made on animals whilst in a torpid state, would be found, in many cases, to heal most readily; and the results of some experiments which I have made lead me to think that these conjectures are well founded, and to hope that you will think the results sufficiently interesting to induce you to do me the honour to lay them before the Royal Society. The experiments were necessarily made upon living animals, but they were confined to animals previously condemned to death; and as their lives were preserved, and their suffering very slight, (certainly not so great as they would have sustained if their lives had been taken away by any of the ordinary methods of killing such animals) I venture to hope that they, in aggregate, rather received benefit than injury. Subjects of different species were employed, chiefly puppies of a few weeks or months old, and the experiments were often repeated, but as the results were all uniform, and as my chief object is to attract the attention of medical men to the subject, I wish to do little more than to state the general results.

EXPERIMENT 1st. Dogs of about a month old were placed under a glass cover, surrounded by water, so as to prevent the ingress of atmospheric air, where their respiration is in a short time ceased, and a part of one ear of each was then taken off; there was no haemorrhage, and the wounds were healed at the end of the third day, without any inflammation having taken place, or the animals having apparently suffered any pain or inconvenience from the operation.

EXPERIMENT 2nd. After the same animals had fully recovered their powers of feeling, a similar part of the other ear of each was taken off; a good deal of blood now flowed from the wounds, and some degree of inflammation followed, and the wounds did not heal until the fifth day.

EXPERIMENT 3rd. An experiment was made similar to No. 1, in every respect, except that the suspension of animation was more suddenly brought on by the agency of sulphuric acid and carbonate of lime. The results in this case were not so satisfactory; some blood escaped from the wounds, and a slight degree of inflammation followed, and the wounds did not heal so rapidly as the first experiment.

EXPERIMENT 4th. Mice, having been confined in a glass tube a foot long, were rendered insensible by carbonic acid gas slowly introduced in small quantities, and one foot from each was taken off; no haemorrhage took place upon the return of sensation, and the wounds appeared quite healed on the third day, without the animals having apparently suffered pain, when they were given liberty.

EXPERIMENT 5th. An adult dog was rendered insensible by means similar to the preceding, and the muscles and blood vessels of one of its legs were divided. There was no haemorrhage from the smaller vessels; a ligature which secured the main artery came away on the fourth day, and the animal recovered without having at any period shown any material symptom of uneasiness. In this experiment animation was suspended during seventeen minutes, allowing respiration occasionally to intervene by means of inflating instruments.

EXPERIMENT 6th. A dog was rendered insensible by the means employed in experiment first, and an incision was made through the muscles of the loin, through which a ligature was passed, and made tight; no appearance of suffering occurred upon the return of animation, nor till the following day, when inflammation came on with subsequent suppuration. The ligature came away on the seventh day, and on the twelfth day the wound was healed.

As the recital of such experiments as those preceding must be as little agreeable to you, as the repetition of them has been to myself, I shall not give a detail of any others, but shall only state the opinions which the aggregate results have led me to entertain. I feel perfectly satisfied that any surgical operation might be performed with quite as much safety upon a subject in an insensible state, as in a sensible state, and that a patient might be kept with perfect safety long enough in an insensible state, for the performance of the most tedious operation. My own experience has also satisfied me that in very many cases the best effects would be produced by the patient's mind being relieved from the anticipation of suffering, and his body from the actual suffering of a severe operation; and I believe that there are few, if any Surgeons who could not operate more skilfully when they were conscious that they were not inflicting pain. There are also many cases in which it would be important to prevent any considerable haemorrhage, and in which the surgeon would feel the advantages of a diminished flow of blood during an operation. I have reason to believe that no injurious consequence would follow if the necessity of the case should call for more than one suspension of animation; for a young growing dog was several times rendered insensible by carbonic acid gas, with intervals of about twenty-four or forty-eight hours, without sustaining, apparently, the slightest injury. Its appetite continued perfectly good, and I ascertained, by weighing it, that it gained weight rapidly. I am not, at present, aware of any source of danger to a patient, from an operation performed during a state of insensibility, which would not operate to the same extent upon a patient in full possession of his powers of suffering, particularly if he were rendered insensible by being simply subjected to respire confined air. I used inflating instruments in one experiment only, and therefore am not prepared to say to what extent such may be used with advantage; but I think it probable that those and the galvanic fluid would operate in restoring animation in some cases. I was prepared to employ galvanic fluid if any case occurred to render the operation of a stimulant necessary, but all the sub-

jects recovered by being simply exposed to the open air; and I feel so confident that animation in the human subject could be safely suspended by proper means, carefully employed, that, (although I could not conscientiously recommend a patient to risk his life in the experiment) I certainly should not hesitate a moment to become the subject of it, if I were under the necessity of suffering any long or severe operation.

I remain, Sir,

Your obedient Servant,

H.H. HICKMAN.

Shiffnal, Aug. 14th, 1824.

Commentary on *TO THE PUBLIC*

The beginning of the Address TO THE PUBLIC was less abrupt than that of the previous letter, possibly in part because Hickman was aiming at a fresh audience. The placing of 'it is' in the first sentence might be interpreted as a slight grammatical affectation.

Hickman's opening statement raises the question: who were the gentlemen of first rate talent who ranked high in the scientific world? What were his contacts with them? How did they advise him to lay this letter before the public and his medical brethren? One might guess that they were Fellows of the Royal Society and that any contact with them would have been through Knight as an intermediary. We do not know how much contact there was between Knight and Hickman beyond Hickman's two letters. Hickman's hope that 'some one or other may be more fortunate...' suggests that he was at least unsure how to prove the safety of suspended animation during surgery in humans.

If Hickman asked for anything in the pamphlet's Address TO THE PUBLIC it was for 'candid discussion and liberality of sentiment' and one can imagine that he hoped for this from the Royal Society. He tried to protect himself against accusations of self-adulation in publishing the letter but, as we shall see later, this rather backfired. In the pamphlet Hickman defines the duties of the physician and surgeon as distinct from those of just the operating surgeon:

The duty and object... of the Physician and Surgeon, is ...the relief of a fellow-creature, by applying certain remedies to the cure of internal affections, or cutting some portion of the body, whereby parts are severed from each other altogether, or relieving cavities of the aggravating cause of disease.

He may have included the physician's duties here in order to widen the discussion, to acknowledge that his practice entailed the application of certain remedies to the cure of internal affections, or in anticipation of his styling himself as a physician in Shifnal.

Hickman ended his Address TO THE PUBLIC with these words:

... if one grain of knowledge can be added to the general fund, to obtain a means for the relief of pain, the labours of the author will be amply rewarded.

Commentary on *A LETTER &c.*

In the second section of the pamphlet Hickman virtually made a direct request, expressing hope that Knight would:

...think the results sufficiently interesting to induce you to do me the honour to lay them before the Royal Society.

But first he restated his approach to the subject:

The facility of suspending animation by carbonic acid gas, and other means, without permanent injury to the subject, having been long known, it appears rather singular that no experiments have hitherto been made with the object of ascertaining whether operations could be successfully performed upon animals whilst in a torpid state; and whether wounds inflicted upon them in such a state would be found to heal with greater or less facility than similar wounds inflicted on the same animals whilst in possession of all their powers of feeling and suffering.

What does that crucial sentence tell us? Hickman evidently believed it well known that carbonic acid gas, and other means, could easily produce suspended animation without causing permanent injury. His handwritten letter tells us that this belief was based on many experiments on suspended animation. Presumably these were reported somewhere in the literature. The same questions raised in the commentary on the handwritten letter crop up again here. To what experiments was he referring? Did the fact that he failed to quote a source mean that he never read the accounts himself? Did he learn about them from hearsay, perhaps when without access to a library or to relevant journals?

In defence of animal experiments
Before describing his experiments (see below) he said that they were:

confined to animals previously condemned to death; and as their lives were preserved, and their suffering very slight, (certainly not so great as they would have sustained if their lives had been taken away by any of the ordinary means of killing such animals) I venture to hope that they had rather received benefit than injury

but after presenting his experiments Hickman added:

As the recital of such experiments as those preceding must be as little agreeable to you, as the repetition of them has been to myself, I shall not give a detail of any others...

Such considerations were not discussed at all in Hickman's handwritten letter of February 1824, which suggests that they were inserted in the pamphlet upon advice – probably proffered by Knight – who between 1816 and 1818 had had correspondence with Sir Joseph Banks about growing reaction among Fellows of the Royal Society against cruelty to animals.

Commentary on the experiments
With the handwritten letter of February (FEB), Hickman presented seven individual experiments. With his printed pamphlet of August (AUG) he presented some individual experiments and some groups of repeated experiments without saying how many animals there were in each group. Some of the individual experiments were probably also included in the groups, but he did not say so.

In separately presenting the two series of experiments, Hickman had differing objectives. He prefaced the FEB experiments by:

From a number of others I have selected the experiments now sent; each is correctly noted in as few words as possible, which I think will prove a vast object.

The AUG Experiments were prefaced by:

Subjects of different species were employed, chiefly puppies of a few weeks or months old, and the experiments were often repeated, but as the results were all

45

uniform, and as my chief object is to attract the attention of other medical men to the subject, I wish to do little more than state the general results.

Experiment 1st. (FEB), dated 20th March, (1823 or before) was presented by Hickman as follows:

I took a puppy a month old and placed it upon a piece of wood surrounded by water over which I put a glass cover to prevent the access of atmospheric air …

This was a case of deliberate asphyxia. Sealing the glass cover would have resulted in a steady reduction of oxygen and accumulation of carbon dioxide. Both would contribute to suspended animation, but Hickman did not discuss mechanisms.

He presented the First (group) Experiment (AUG), without stating how many dogs were used, thus:

Dogs of about a month old were placed under a glass cover, surrounded by water, so as to prevent the ingress of atmospheric air …

Hickman thus demonstrated that by deprivation of atmospheric air alone he could render puppies apparently insensible and without pain during surgery. Perhaps he thought it appeared less cruel to experiment on 'dogs' a month old than on 'puppies' a month old. Hickman might with advantage have dwelt upon the duration and severity of the 'great marks of uneasiness' and upon the difficulty in breathing, but he would have viewed this against an early nineteenth-century perspective in comparison with the distress caused by naked surgery.

Were we to witness the same experiments, our point of reference would be normal respiration against which the animals' respiratory distress would probably be unacceptable. Times quoted in the first (FEB) experiments were omitted from the second (AUG) series; it would have been of interest to know the duration of surgery and of recovery, the size of the animal and the capacity of the glass cover.

The single Experiment 1st. (FEB) was more informative than the corresponding 1st (group) Experiment (AUG). With regard to the group presentation, one cannot help questioning the alleged uniformity of the results. It is perhaps surprising that Hickman should apparently have thought the group experiments more likely to attract the favourable attention of other medical men.

To place a human subject beneath a glass cover in order induce suspended animation by asphyxia during surgery was obviously impractical, and this may have led Hickman to consider the administration of carbon dioxide (second experiment [FEB]), but there is no evidence of this. He did not discuss how carbon dioxide might be administered to man. However, in his second February experiment, he did expose the puppy 'to carbon dioxide produced by the reaction of sulphuric acid and carbonate of lime'.

In the Second (group) Experiment (AUG), he waited until those in the first group had recovered and then removed a similar part of the other ear without asphyxia or carbonic acid gas. Presumably he would have regarded this as the control experiment.

For the Third Experiment (FEB), performed on 6th April, he repeated the same asphyxial procedure as in the first experiment, but made no specific comment about pain relief during surgery. He seemed more concerned about the prevention of bleeding and inflammation.

For the Third (group) Experiment (AUG) he used carbon dioxide to produce suspended animation rapidly and excised one ear. The results were said to be less satisfactory than in the first group of experiments, some blood escaping and a slight degree of inflammation following.

For the Fourth Experiment (FEB) he confined a mouse beneath a glass, surrounded by water. By means of a small tube a foot long he passed carbonic acid gas very slowly and in small quantities into the glass. Respiration ceased in three minutes. He cut off all its legs at the first joint and plunged it into a basin of cold water. The animal immediately recovered and ran about the table apparently without pain. The stumps soon healed and he gave it liberty after a fortnight. This experiment seems to belie Hickman's concern about the welfare of the animals.

He treated mice in the same way in the corresponding Sixth (group) Experiment (AUG), except that he took off only one foot from each. This rather suggests that someone protested at the report on the mouse left with four stumps (FEB) and later left to fend for itself. If that was so, one cannot help wondering how many more multi-amputations Hickman performed before receiving a protest.

For the Fifth Experiment (FEB) Hickman exposed an adult dog to carbon dioxide quickly prepared and in large quantity, and animation was suspended for seventeen minutes. Respiration was allowed occasionally to intervene using inflating instruments. Did he use bellows and some form of intubation of the trachea?

The Fifth Experiment (AUG) described in the printed letter appears to have been very similar except that the carbon dioxide was said to be slowly prepared and in small quantity. But as the times quoted were the same and inflating instruments were again used, this might have been precisely the same experiment in the same animal, one of the descriptions of carbon dioxide production and quantity being in error.

His Sixth Experiment (AUG) concerned a single dog which was asphyxiated beneath a glass cover, as in the first printed experiment. An incision was made through the muscles of the loin, through which a ligature was passed and made tight. There was no appearance of suffering when animation returned. This seems to be his only comment on postoperative pain.

With his manuscript letter there was a Seventh Experiment (FEB) in which he filled a glass globe with gas exhaled from his own lungs and into which he put a kitten. He took off its ear and tail after twenty seconds – rather soon. There was no appearance of pain.

Rejection in England

Distaste by the public and scientists for apparently cruel animal experimentation, clearly foreseen by Hickman, and presumably by Knight, had been evident in the Royal Society's *Transactions* a short time before, and may have provided the key to the rejection of his work in his own country. Dr. Andrew Wilson Philip of Worcester was blackballed by The Royal Society following his attempts to present his experiments involving division of the vagus nerves of live rabbits between 1816 and 1820[2, 3].

It is interesting to note that following an 1822 Act of Parliament aimed at lessening cruelty to animals, the Society (later the Royal Society) for the Prevention of Cruelty to Animals was founded in 1824, just as Hickman was most active. We do not know who first suggested that Hickman's experiments might be worthy of being laid before the Royal Society. Maybe Knight had already talked informally with some of its Fellows. In that case an explanation is required for the discrepancy between the presumption of a favourable reception (implied by the evident proposal to present them to that body) and the subsequent lack of appreciation and consistent ridicule of Hickman's work.

Under the title 'Surgical Experiments' the *Gentleman's Magazine*[4] published a letter which, after describing Hickman's claims, continued: *(He) says he should not hesitate a moment to become the subject of the experiment he recommends, if he were under the necessity of suffering any severe operation. Notwithstanding Dr Hickman's confidence, it may be doubted whether the pain of his operation, and especially in the recovery, would not equal or perhaps surpass that experienced in the usual mode of operation.*

This was measured and polite compared with the vituperative and dismissive letter which appeared in *The Lancet* of 4th February 1826[5]:

> *… can be for a moment suppose that any <u>medical man</u> of sense and judgment will be so far led away by a proposal so utterly at variance with all he has ever heard, saw, or read, of the deleterious effects of respiring the fixed air, even for a short time, as to believe, for a moment, that this letter was published with any intention of benefiting mankind; …*
>
> *As for that large portion of society, who do not belong to the medical profession, does he suppose that they would not laugh him to scorn if he were to recommend a man who was about to have a tooth drawn to be previously hanged, drowned, or smothered for a few minutes, in order that he may feel no pain during the operation?*

Referring to Hickman's willingness to 'become the subject of it' if he were to need an operation, the writer continues:

> *How magnanimous, what a noble declaration, as though he does not know, that if he were weak enough to make such a proposal (which in any case I know he would not be, when really about to undergo an operation) that it would, I sincerely hope, and believe, for the credit of the profession, be utterly impossible to find any surgeon so <u>great a fool</u>, and so unwarrantably bold as to undertake that operation on such terms.*
>
> *Now I do fervently hope that the letter itself may be a complete hoax, and not written by Dr Hickman; for, in this age of science and gentlemanly acquirement, I feel assured, that no man who has any claim to the honourable appellation of Doctor of Physic would so far disgrace both his profession and himself by writing such a <u>tissue of quackery</u>, which he himself, and every medical man must know is (to say the least) <u>humbug.</u>*
> > *… I am, &c*
> > > *Antiquack*

It was against this background that Hickman, having failed to gain any support for his ideas in England, took the exceptional step of seeking assistance from the Medical Schools in Paris through a direct approach to Charles X, King of France.

References
1. Loudon I. *Medical care and the General Practitioner 1750-1850*. Oxford Clarendon Press 1986.
2. Smith W.D.A. Further light on Hickman and his times. *Brit. J. Anaesth.* 1970; **42**: 445-458.
3. McMenemy W.H. Alexander Philips Wilson Philip (1770-1847), physiologist and physician. *J. Hist. Med.* 1958; **13**, 289-328.
4. Surgical Experiments. *Gentleman's Magazine;* Jan-June 1825; **95**; 628.
5. Antiquack. *Lancet;* Feb. 4th 1826; **9**: 646-647.

CHAPTER SIX

Hickman in France;
a plea to Charles X in Paris

Hickman left for Paris in April 1828 and shortly after arriving, he wrote home to Eliza, his wife. The letter is reproduced here in full because it provides us with one of the few glimpses of Hickman the family man.

My dear Eliza   *Paris April 21st, 1828,*
Quite safe have I arrived here after one of the most laughable journeys that can possibly be imagined, and I lose no time in giving you the information, but as the particulars will serve me to make a small volume, for the amusement of you and other friends on my return, at leisure hours, I shall defer giving you a description further that we had a dreadful sea from Dover to Calais and every passenger on board, except myself, was <u>dreadfully sick</u>, it was an awfully grand passage, though safe, to me most delightful. What I have seen of Paris which has not been a little for the time, I have seen nothing in my life like it, it seems to be a place of pleasure and everything to please the Eye and gratify the senses – As I don't know how John may be suited as to Lodgings I have sent for him to my Hotel, which every house is called here, and I expect him every minute – I wrote from Dover and Calais and I hope you got the Letters, and that there is one on the road now for me – I hope to God your ankle is doing well and let me beg to you to tell me exactly how it is, if so, and the children are well I shall be happy, and as soon as I can hear from Glover to whom I shall write by this post I shall think of returning, about the time you named – Jack is this moment arrived and most utterly astonished and delighted to see me – He is very well – Kiss the dear Baby for me, I should like to see them though as the Journey is so easily and safely performed I content myself by knowing they are well which I can do by your writing every week, which I shall do to you – and please God we live and things turn out as I think they will, you shall see this place – I found no difficulty in coming along I could make myself tolerably well understood and hold a pretty fair conversation as soon as my ear became accustomed to the sound <u>a la francais</u> – If you have not written, write to me immediately – and my next Lr. shall give you some information as to my progress <u>en France</u> – With kindest love to all, believe me my dearest love yours ever affectionately.
                        H. Hickman
Direct to John.

Editors' Note:
The Glovers (father and two sons) Cartwright[1] draws attention to the names 'John' and 'Glover' and points out that John Glover (1767-1849) with his sons John jun. and William were English painters who were active in Paris, enjoying the patronage of the French Royal family. A certain Joseph Glover described as the elder brother of John, father of William, lived at Astley, a village lying three miles equidistant between Eliza's family home at Leigh Court, and Stourport on Severn where Hickman was almost certainly

apprenticed. It must be possible, if not highly likely, that the Glover family was known to both Hickman and Eliza. If so the Glovers may have encouraged Hickman to go to France and with their Royal contacts, suggested and facilitated his direct approach to Charles X. Denis seems, uncharacteristically, to have overlooked Cartwright's findings.

Some time elapsed before Hickman presented his petition to Charles X and a handwritten draft or copy of it survives (Appendix A, p70), but how closely it corresponds with the original actually sent is not known. It is noteworthy (and it was noted at the time) that it was written in English. The scribe seemed primarily concerned with etiquette and with conveying a broad idea of Hickman's aspirations and methods. Detail was limited, and had the Academy granted Hickman's wishes it would have had to be supplemented. There may have been supplementary documentation which has not survived, or he may have intended to provide detail verbally, but on his first visit to France he could have found difficulty in communication. Some indication of his linguistic ability appears in the letter to Eliza:

> *I could make myself tolerably well understood and hold a pretty fair conversation as soon as my ear became accustomed to the sound a la francais* [sic].

He was probably fluent enough for casual social exchanges but he could have been at a disadvantage when coping with professional confrontation. The King of France forwarded Hickman's petition to the Académie Royale de Médicine. It would be interesting to know if there were any precedents for such a referral, but it seems unlikely because the Academy of Medicine had not been established until 1820 and the King had been on the throne for only four years.

Hickman, his letter and the Académie Royale.
According to the register at the Ministry of the Interior, Hickman's letter to the King was dated 7th August. Its receipt was registered on 8th August 1828. It was forwarded to the Académie Royale de Médicine on 31st August and Hickman was informed of this[1]. At a meeting held at the Academy on 23rd September 1828, M. Gerardin reported on a 'letter' written to His Majesty Charles X by Mr Hickman, a London Surgeon. After a brief reference to Hickman's animal experiments, M. Gerardin explained that Hickman was desirous of obtaining the co-operation of the leading Physicians and Surgeons in Paris, in order to make the same experiments on the human subject. The Minutes ended:

> *This letter will be communicated to l'Académie reunie* – [plenary session].

In 1828 the Academy was subdivided into three sections, and there is evidence that M. Gerardin belonged to the Section of Medicine. The next relevant meeting, on 21st October 1828, was presumably that of the combined sections (plenary session). The report of its committee, consisting of Mm. Dubois, Richerand, Merat, Segalles and Ribes, was either not prepared or has disappeared without trace.

Born in 1757 with the title Count of Artois, **Charles X of France (reigned 1824-1830)** was the grandson of Louis XV and brother of Louis XVI and Louis XVIII. His encouragement of Louis XVI's attempts to control the revolutionaries contributed to the King's downfall and Charles himself had to leave France in 1789 for Germany, Italy, England and Scotland, where George III allowed him to live at Holyrood. Returning to France after Waterloo, he encouraged his brother, Louis XVIII, in his ultra-royalist attitude, and continued in this way after the latter's death in 1824. Charles's elaborate coronation at Rheims (the last to take place in France) and his continued belief in the divine right of kings, turned the nation against him and he was forced to abdicate by the July Revolution of 1830 when he briefly returned to Britain, and later to Prague to die in the present-day Slovenia in 1836.

Minutes of Meetings in 1828 and 1847

The Meeting 'reunie' of 21st October 1828, which attended to Hickman's letter, was remembered by M. Gerardin at another meeting nineteen years later, in 1847. The Minutes of this 1847 meeting tell us that M. Gerardin recalled Hickman's 'letter' to Charles X causing:

> *A sensation in the Academy, some members treating it with contempt. But Baron Larrey offered to try the experiment.*

Why these expressions of 'sensation' and 'contempt'? Were they caused by the very idea of painless surgery, by the potential hazards of inducing insensibility or suspended animation, by the means proposed, or was it just too much to accept all at once? If M. Gerardin's memory was correct, Baron Larrey was probably proposing to refer the matter to the Surgical Section of the Academy. This raises questions: were Minutes of the different Sections kept separately? If so, were they searched in 1911 and 1930? What would have been the outcome had Hickman's proposals been referred to the Surgical Section?

The records of the Meeting 'reunie' of October 1828 state that Hickman:

> *…Made numerous experiments on animals, and was desirous of obtaining the co-operation of the leading physicians and surgeons in Paris in order to make the same experiments on the human subject…. Mr Hickman has already tried the method on animals and he wishes to carry out the experiment before the famous surgeons of the capital.*

The wording is slightly ambiguous, but it seems that Hickman was proposing to get straight into human experiments without first repeating any of the work on animals. Only Baron Larrey, then sixty-two years old, seemed to have impressed the reporter with his open mindedness, but it is uncertain what Larrey actually said or meant. His comments were not minuted. We have only the minuted remains of Gerardin's memory nineteen years after the event. Larrey may have been volunteering just to take an interest, to repeat animal, and other, experiments, or even volunteer as an experimental subject.

It has been noted that six months later, in April 1829, the French surgeon Jules-Germain Cloquet (1790-1883), reported to L'Académie his case of a painless mastectomy in a mesmerised patient. Baron Larrey was present at this meeting, and made some very critical comments (see Chapter 3). However, his criticism did not seem to generate quite the same degree of ridicule that Hickman's petition had produced when it was discussed six month earlier. If that interpretation is correct, what was it about Hickman's presentation that made it appear even less acceptable than mesmerism?

Academicians may have felt that Hickman's proposed untried-in-man induction of suspended animation, by whatever means, was quite preposterous, whereas mesmerism at least had a lively history and, although largely rejected by the medical fraternity, its flame was still alight. The concept of animal magnetism was probably acceptable to many Frenchmen; the idea of inhaling carbonic acid gas, or of asphyxia to produce insensibility during surgery probably was not. Vocabularies had accepted 'mesmerism' and 'animal magnetism'. People had some idea what they meant. The imprint of 'anaesthesia' on language had not occurred and most 'thinking' requires words. Cloquet's account was not followed by any similar reports of painless operations.

A reproduction of the manuscript and a printed transcription of a copy or a draft of Hickman's appeal to Charles X *(figure 8, p53)* follow Hickman's pamphlet in the *Souvenir*, published in 1930 for the Hickman Centenary Exhibition. It is in English and nearly eight hundred words long, on just over two pages of manuscript. The manuscript is neatly folded and finely written, apart from the address beneath Hickman's signature, which was evidently added later with a coarser quill. It is not known whether Hickman found a model on which to base this letter, whether he obtained advice on its composition or why he did not get it written or translated into French. (When the petition was found in 1847 by M. Gerardin[2], he confirmed that it was in English). The French may well have been confused about Hickman's professional interests and standing for he began his second paragraph:

> *Permit me, Sire, to state that I am a British Physician, Member of the Royal College of Surgeons, London, who has visited Paris in part for the purpose of bringing to completion a discovery, to which I have been led by a course of observations and experiments on suspended animation.*

The other purpose of his visit is unknown. It is not surprising that he was sometimes referred to as an English Physician and sometimes as a London Surgeon.

He presented his case thus:

> *This object has engaged my practical attention during several years: it appears demonstrable that the hitherto most agonising, dangerous and delicate surgical operations may now be performed, with perfect safety and exemption from pain, on brute animals in a state of suspended animation. Hence it is to be strongly inferred, by analogy, that the same salutary effects may be produced on the human frame, when rendered insensible by means of the introduction of certain gases into the lungs. I have discovered a number of facts connected with this important subject, and I wish to bestow them upon society.*

Hickman explained:

> *I have ventured on the liberty of praying your majesty to be pleased, by an express intimation, or command, on the subject, to permit me to develop my ideas on operations in a state of suspended animation, in the presence of Your Majesty's Medical and Surgical schools, that I may have the benefit of their eminent and assembled talent, and emulous co-operation.*

Then before closing he added:

> *It is also my desire, at a fit opportunity, to solicit the honour of presenting to Your Majesty, in person, if Your Majesty will condescend to receive it, a Book containing an account of my discovery which, as far as I know or can learn, has entirely originated with myself; and should my labours meet with the approbation of Charles the Tenth, I shall ever enjoy the grateful satisfaction of believing that I have devoted myself to my profession to a distinguished and happy end...*

A book

Previous searches have failed to find the actual petition sent to Charles X, or the book that Hickman offered him. Only the one copy of the pamphlet ('To the Public' etc) has survived. We do not know the contents of the gift Hickman offered or even whether Charles X accepted it. One can imagine that Hickman had prepared for him a specially bound copy of the pamphlet, with extra leaves for a manuscript history of the project, but we do not know that and, as we have seen, Hickman had good reason to be disappointed with the pamphlet. Whatever form this book took, it would now make fascinating reading. Should it ever be found, it would be of great interest to see whether it gave

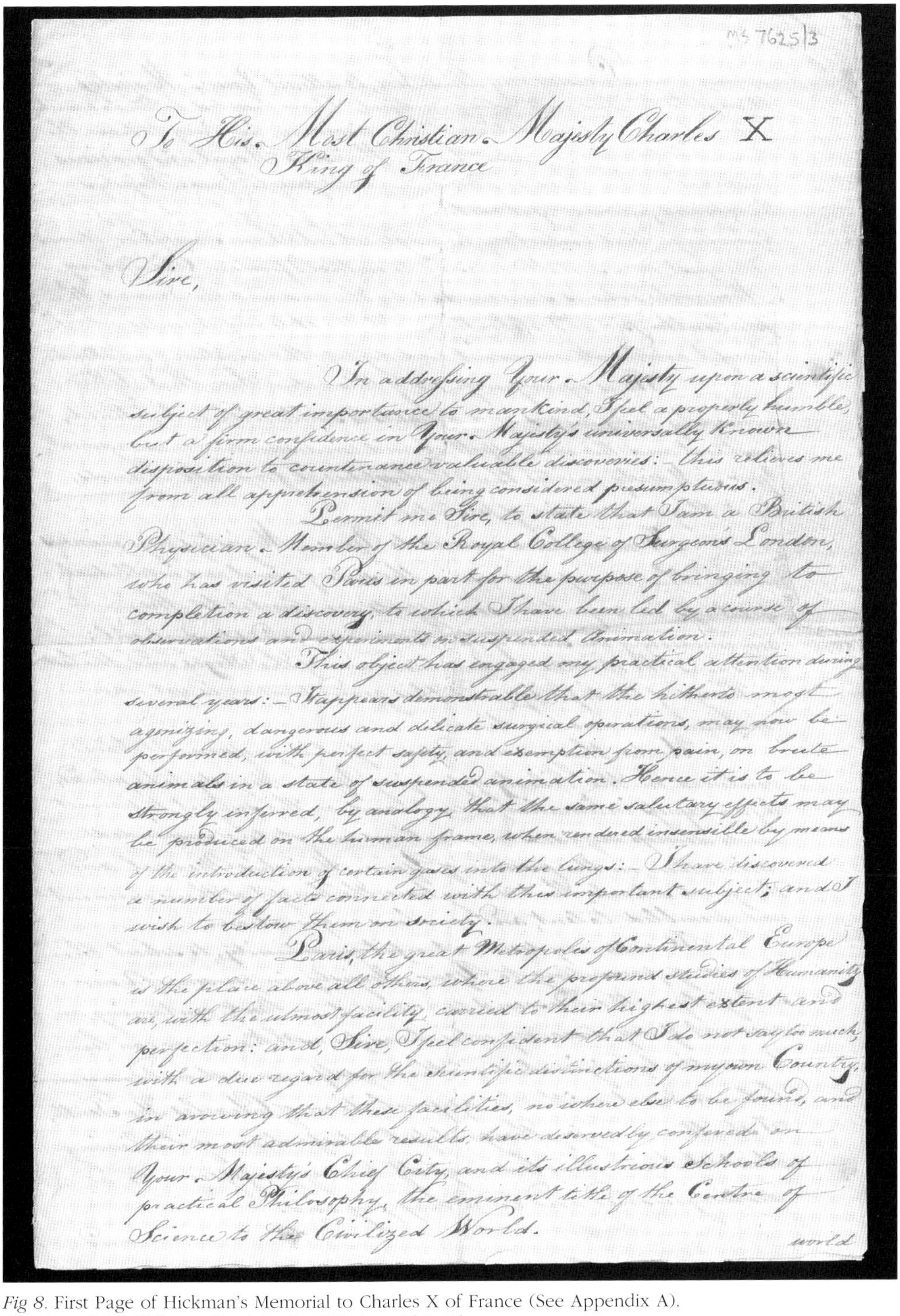

To His Most Christian Majesty Charles X
King of France

Sire,

In addressing Your Majesty upon a scientific subject of great importance to mankind, I feel a properly humble, but a firm confidence in Your Majesty's universally known disposition to countenance valuable discoveries: this relieves me from all apprehension of being considered presumptuous.

Permit me Sire, to state that I am a British Physician, Member of the Royal College of Surgeons London; who has visited Paris in part for the purpose of bringing to completion a discovery, to which I have been led by a course of observations and experiments on suspended animation.

This object has engaged my practical attention during several years:—It appears demonstrable that the hitherto most agonizing, dangerous and delicate surgical operations, may now be performed, with perfect safety and exemption from pain, on brute animals in a state of suspended animation. Hence it is to be strongly inferred, by analogy, that the same salutary effects may be produced on the human frame, when rendered insensible by means of the introduction of certain gases into the lungs:—I have discovered a number of facts connected with this important subject; and I wish to bestow them on society.

Paris, the great Metropolis of Continental Europe is the place above all others, where the profound studies of Humanity are, with the utmost facility, carried to their highest extent and perfection: and, Sire, I feel confident that I do not say too much, with a due regard for the scientific distinctions of my own Country, in avowing that these facilities, no where else to be found, and their most admirable results have deservedly conferred on Your Majesty's Chief City, and its illustrious Schools of practical Philosophy, the eminent title of the Centre of Science to the Civilized World.

world

Fig 8. First Page of Hickman's Memorial to Charles X of France (See Appendix A).
Courtesy of the Wellcome Trust Medical Photographic Library.

details of any advances made by Hickman between 1824 and 1828, and especially whether he had given practical thought to the induction of suspended animation in humans. There may be a clue. Accounts of the relevant meetings of the Royal Academy of Medicine all refer to the 'methodical induction of certain gases into the lungs' and refer to the 'systematic introduction of certain gases into the lungs'. Nowhere in either of his letters to T.A. Knight or in his petition to Charles X did Hickman use the words methodical or systematic. In the petition he wrote 'by means of the introduction of certain gases into the lungs'. Who first introduced methodical and on what grounds? How did he manufacture or get his gases? What was the method by which the gases were introduced into the lungs? Could this have been in the 'Book'? Could Charles X have commanded Hickman to forward his 'Book' to the Academy?

A present

Hickman spent at least six months in Paris. We can only speculate how he managed to support himself in a fashionable capital city for so long, but he was certainly not penniless. His account books show a business-like attitude to his practices in Ludlow and Shifnal and reveal, for instance, that he charged family members the standard rate for his services. When he arrived in Paris, he may have received some help, possibly board and lodging, from the Glovers and perhaps he was able to find patients amongst expatriate British. In July, he bought an amethyst and citrine bracelet for Eliza (*see inside front cover*) so clearly he could afford the occasional extravagance. The deliciously coy inscription on the accompanying card reads:

> *For Mrs. Hickman with the kind love of a gentleman she has a slight knowledge of*
> *– bought in the Palais Royale July 31, -28*

Towards the end of his stay, the hope expressed in his letter to Eliza that she might join him was realised, and with another pen he added:

> *and given to her Nov 10 at half past 9 o'clock at Meurice Hotel, Paris.*

The bracelet has been passed down through the female line and is now in the possession of Mrs Jean Scragg, Hickman's great, great granddaughter.

References

1. Cartwright F.F. *The English Pioneers of Anaesthesia (Beddoes, Davy and Hickman)* p.293. Bristol, John Wright & Sons 1952.

2. Souvenir: *Henry Hill Hickman Centenary Exhibition 1830-1930*. London: Wellcome Foundation Ltd 1930.

3. Anonymous. *Bulletin de l'Académie Royale de Médecine*. 1846-47; Tom. **XII**: 418-419.

CHAPTER SEVEN

Hickman's Centenary

Honour a physician with the honour due unto him

Thompson, Curator of the Wellcome Historical Medical Museum, began research into Hickman about 1911, and an editorial entitled *An Unfinished Chapter in the History of Anaesthesia* appeared in the British Medical Journal (BMJ) towards the end of that year[1]. It quoted two pertinent references from the second volume of the *Works of Sir James Young Simpson*[2]:

> *Sir H. Davy recommended … nitrous oxide… Dr Hickman also, in 1828, suggested the inhalation of carbon dioxide, as a means of producing insensibility in surgical experiments.*

The other reference originated in a letter of 1870 to Dr Jacob Bigelow in which Simpson suggested carbonic acid:

> *In imitation of the experiments performed for ages on the poor dogs at the Grotto del Cane.* (Chapter 3)

The editorial went on to quote from a pamphlet entitled *Memoranda Relating to the discovery of Surgical Anaesthesia, and Dr William T.G. Morton's Relation to this event* by Dr W.J. Morton in which he wrote:

> *Among actual operators who produced anaesthesia for surgical operations (before 1846) was Dauriol who specifies five cases of painless operations under the effect of anodyne vapours and, more remarkably, Hickman, a surgeon of London who, in 1828, in a letter to the French Academy of Medicine, published his results and described a method of 'suspending sensibility by the methodical introduction of certain gases into the lungs' during which 'the most delicate and dangerous operations are performed without producing pain in the individuals submitted to them'.*

The 1911 editorial, in effect, had two authors – C.J.S. Thompson, who was named, and a Dr Taylor. Readers would have realised that the curiosity of these authors had been aroused by the writings of Morton and Simpson, and that research into Hickman was continuing and being communicated by Thompson. They might also have wondered how Simpson and Morton learned about Drs Dauriol and Hickman. Several clues were available in 1847. Both *The Lancet* and the *Boston Medical and Surgical Journal* published notices of mention of Dr Dauriol's work in the *Journal de Toulouse*, although the author has not been able to identify the primary reference. One of these notices could have been Morton's source of information on Dr Dauriol.

The first full account of Hickman's work was published in the BMJ over the initials C.J.S.T. in 1912, in readiness for an Exhibition planned to coincide with the International Medical Congress in London in 1913[3]. The First World War then intervened. In 1926 Buxton, in a series of historical notes, referred to Hickman in the British Journal of

Anaesthesia[4] and freely acknowledged Thompson's original research but both writers mistakenly dated Hickman's burial as 1829. Towards the end of the 1920s, L.W.G. Malcolm, Thompson's successor at the Wellcome Museum, collected all available material for the Museum's Hickman Centenary Exhibition of 1930, for which a Souvenir Volume was produced[5].

Preparations for the Centenary

The first printed reminder of the Centenary appeared in 1927, in a letter to the BMJ from the Rev F. Wayland Joyce[6]. Joyce was Rector of Burford, close to Tenbury Wells where Hickman died. He pleaded for recognition of; *the forgotten benefactor and great medical pioneer, Henry Hill Hickman,* and if he had not remonstrated with the English medical faculty the centenary could have been passed over. He continued:

> *... is it not reasonable to hope that those who represent the English medical faculty will do something to recognise the debt which we all owe to one of our greatest medical pioneers? The least that might be done is that his dilapidated gravestone should be restored, with some suitable inscription perpetuating his name, and expressing the honour long overdue to a great human benefactor, one withal English born and English bred...*

Response to that letter might have been entirely negative. Critics might have seen little reason to feel greatly indebted to Hickman. They might have seen him as a pioneer but not as one of the greatest. He did not convince others of the potential value of insensibility during surgery and it might be argued, not unreasonably, that suspended animation and the inhalation of carbonic acid were dangerous. Furthermore Hickman had made his point only in a few animals. However, the Section of Anaesthetics, Royal Society of Medicine (RSM) responded positively to Joyce's plea. Minutes of Council reveal nothing of discussions behind the scenes but it seems that, in 1930, the clergy was better able to persuade the medical faculty to take notice of Hickman, than he had been able to persuade his contemporaries a century earlier to explore his ideas about surgery without pain.

Dr Cecil Hughes, in 1927 President of the Section of Anaesthetics, took up the challenge. He liaised with the Wellcome Historical Medical Museum and other organisations and in 1928 acted as Honorary Secretary of a committee set up to collect funds, under the chairmanship of Lord Dawson of Penn. The Fund was used for a Hickman Medal, to renovate the Hickman family tombstone and to install a commemorative tablet in the Parish Church Bromfield. At the annual dinner of the RSM, held at the Mayfair Hotel in November 1928, Hickman received further recognition and Thompson's research was acknowledged. Lord Dawson, President of the RSM, was in the chair and the guests of honour were Mr Winston Churchill and Mr Rudyard Kipling.

However, not everyone maintained enthusiasm for the centenary celebrations. In 1928, Layton protested in the BMJ[7] that general anaesthesia was known centuries before Hickman and quoted Thomas Middleton (c.1570-1627):

> *I'll initiate the pities of the old surgeons to this lost limb, who, ere they show their art, cast one asleep, then cut the diseased part.*

The Historical Medical Museum's conservator, L.W.G. Malcolm, reported in a memo to Sir Henry Wellcome that according to a conversation with a representative of the RSM:

> *Nearly everybody was rather tired of hearing about Hickman .... he did not occupy such a prominent place as to justify a very big celebration ... The real reason*

for bringing Hickman into prominence… [was] as an excuse … to endow an International Medal for work done in anaesthesia.

We cannot be sure whether the unidentified representative of the RSM was speaking for himself or for his colleagues, or conveying what he or Malcolm felt Sir Henry might like to hear. That memo belonged to the inter-war period when contemporary attitudes and lack of resources contributed to lack of basic research. Mushin left the following comment on anaesthesia at the time[8]:

Between the two world wars interest in anaesthesia was confined to a mere handful of men who had to stand up to what almost amounted to the contempt of his colleagues, because it was still widely held everywhere in Europe and the United States that anaesthesia was an occupation that hardly demanded a medical education.

The Celebrations

Eighteen months later, the centenary of Hickman's death was celebrated with respect and in style. There were letters, annotations and leading articles in the *BMJ*[9-14], *The Lancet*[15-20], and *The Times*[21-26]. The Hickman Fund had been launched, closed and allocated. Hickman's grave was restored, its tombstone replaced, and Eric Gill was commissioned to engrave a memorial tablet. The Wellcome Historical Medical Museum mounted a special Hickman Centenary Exhibition at 54 Wigmore Street, London, and published a Souvenir Volume to go with it[5]. The Exhibition was opened by Lord Dawson of Penn on 2nd April, and *The Times* reported his opening address as comparing Hickman with Jenner (1749-1823)[24].

Three days after the opening of the Centenary Exhibition, at 2.45 pm on 5th April 1930, the exact centenary of Hickman's burial, three doctors, followed by the Lord Bishop of Hereford, the clergy and the choir, formed a procession from the gatehouse to Bromfield Parish Church *(inside back cover)*. In the congregation were eleven descendants of Hickman; also the Earl of Plymouth and Lt Col Windsor Clive, MP and his wife. There were representatives of the Birmingham Dental School, of the Hereford Division of the British Medical Association, the Hickman Memorial Fund and the Section of Anaesthetics; Royal Society of Medicine including four of its Past Presidents – Sir Francis Shipway, Dr Z. Mennell, Dr Ashley Daly and Dr H.E.G. Boyle, and also Drs Blake, F.W. Cheese and W.H. Farmer. Just as the congregation were singing the opening words of the hymn; *Oh God, our help in ages past* … Sir St. Clair Thompson unveiled Eric Gill's* memorial tablet which, according to its inscription was placed, *(inside back cover)*:

at the initiative of the Section of Anaesthetics of the Royal Society of Medicine as a Centenary tribute to the memory of the earliest known pioneer of Anaesthesia by Inhalation.

The Lesson from Ecclesiasticus, xxxviii, 1-14, provided the title for this chapter and forms the penultimate line of the inscription on Gill's tablet.

---

* **Eric Gill (1882-1940)** Gill is described as the greatest artist-craftsman of the twentieth-century whose typefaces Gill Sans Serif and Perpetua are in worldwide use. He was a draughtsman and wood engraver of subtlety and skill and a sculptor whose figures reflected the eroticism of his own life. He wrote and proselytised about his belief in the value of making by hand, as opposed to industrialisation and can be compared with William Morris in the nineteenth-century. *However, he declined the opportunity of designing the Hickman Medal so it went to T.H. Paget (for a fee of 40 guineas).*

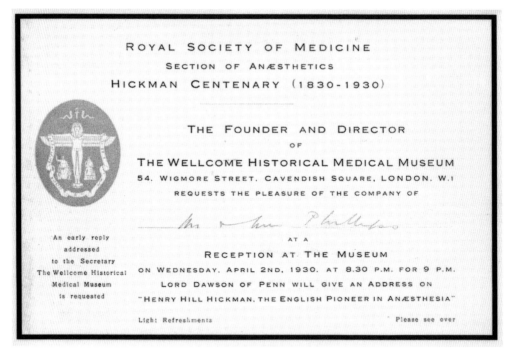

ROYAL SOCIETY OF MEDICINE

SECTION OF ANÆSTHETICS

HICKMAN CENTENARY (1830-1930)

THE FOUNDER AND DIRECTOR
OF
THE WELLCOME HISTORICAL MEDICAL MUSEUM
54. WIGMORE STREET. CAVENDISH SQUARE, LONDON. W.1
REQUESTS THE PLEASURE OF THE COMPANY OF

AT A
RECEPTION AT THE MUSEUM
ON WEDNESDAY. APRIL 2ND, 1930. AT 8.30 P.M. FOR 9 P.M.
LORD DAWSON OF PENN WILL GIVE AN ADDRESS ON
"HENRY HILL HICKMAN. THE ENGLISH PIONEER IN ANÆSTHESIA"

An early reply
addressed
to the Secretary
The Wellcome Historical
Medical Museum
is requested

Light Refreshments   Please see over

Fig 9. Invitation to Hickman Centenary for Mr (grandson) & Mrs Hickman Phillips. *Courtesy of Tenbury Museum.*

The Souvenir

The Henry Hill Hickman Centenary Exhibition 1830-1930 Souvenir carried on the title page the name of Henry S. Wellcome, Director of the Wellcome Historical Medical Museum and L.W.G. Malcolm, its Conservator. Authorship of the *Souvenir* was not attributed[1]. The *Souvenir* was what it said it was; a souvenir, a memento of an event. Although there are doubts about its dating of meetings of the French Royal Academy of Medicine, and other reservations, the *Souvenir* provided an invaluable collection of Hickmanalia, some of which had not been published before and some not since Hickman's time.

A Preface by Dr John D. Comrie, the medical historian, recalled that the Wellcome Historical Medical Museum resulted from the researches of Dr Henry S. Wellcome, and that it was organised in connection with the Section of the History of Medicine at the International Congress held in London in 1913. Comrie mentioned, but did not specify researches by Dr Wellcome *for evidences of agents employed by mankind throughout the ages to lull and numb the senses, and to alleviate pain and suffering*. In particular he mentioned the revelation of *certain recorded documents relating to Hickman's part in the History of Anaesthesia*. He said that documents dealing with the investigations of Henry Hill Hickman were found among the Archives in Paris, while others were obtained from members of Hickman's family in England. This material was added to the Historical Medical Museum but had not previously been published in full. He expressed the opinion that although Hickman never anaesthetised a human subject, he deserved credit for having been the first to prove that pain during operations could be abolished by the inhalation of a gas.

A Foreword was contributed by Dr Dudley Wilmot Buxton who, incidentally, had been President of the Section of Anaesthetics of the XVIIth International Medical Congress held in London in 1913[27]. Buxton began his foreword with the observation that:

It is extremely difficult to appraise justly the work of Henry Hill Hickman...

Yet he ended the same opening paragraph by picturing Hickman as:

The central figure, around (whom) gradually have become grouped those things which have grown into modern anaesthesia.

Buxton was full of praise for Hickman's courage, his total self-abnegation, his inspiration and the 'accuracy' of his experiments. At the foot of Buxton's first page we find:

When we trace his footprints in the scanty sands of his brief life we find how much he accomplished and we recognise...the man was able to leave an indelible impress on the science of all time...

Commentary on Buxton's Foreword

There is little evidence that Hickman actually influenced the discovery or the development of anaesthesia. By the time Hickman himself was rediscovered in 1911, ether anaesthesia had been practised for 67 years. No further research on him was reported between 1913 and 1930. Up to 1930, therefore, one would not expect anyone to have regarded Hickman as a 'central figure'. It is doubtful whether more than a few gave much thought to him, except perhaps when visiting the Wellcome Historical Medical Museum. One might even express surprise that his centenary was celebrated. In 1930 the point could have been made that the Centenary and the *Souvenir* owed much to their prompters and to the groundwork of Thompson in 1911 and 1912[1,3]. Buxton touched upon the background of rapidly increasing knowledge of the chemistry of gases through the work of Lavoisier, Priestley, Beddoes and Davy. He wrote:

No doubt Hickman knew all there was to be known on the subject...

But we know little for certain about what he did know, or think. According to Buxton:

Hickman recognised that vapours introduced into the lungs and thence into the circulation of the blood should provide a means of ensuring sleep for sufferers who had to face the surgeon's knife. He grasped the principle – the method was to follow.

That statement is open to question. There is little evidence that Hickman used or even considered using vapours. He did not mention them in either of his letters to Knight or in the surviving version of his petition to Charles X. Relevant records written within Hickman's lifetime used the word 'gas' or 'gaz' and not 'vapour'. The word 'vapour' first came to notice in the editorial of 1911[1], in its account of M. Gerardin in 1847 recalling Hickman's approach to the Academy in 1828. If M. Gerardin really did refer to 'vapours' in 1847 it was quite likely a slip of the tongue related to the then very recent discovery of ether anaesthesia. Ether vapour may also have been much in Thompson's mind while preparing for the Medical Historical Exhibition. It may also have been that Taylor and Thompson (authors of the editorial) were not too clear about the difference between a gas and a vapour, but that should not have applied to Buxton who was a very senior and much respected anaesthetist.

Whether Hickman used gases or vapours, he did not write that, after their introduction into the lungs they then entered the circulation. This may seem fairly obvious to us now but we do not know what mechanisms, if any, Hickman imagined between inhalation of a gas and the effects it produced. He did not appear to anticipate that vapours or gases introduced into the lungs should of necessity provide a means of ensuring sleep. His thinking seemed to begin with contemplation of the state of suspended animation (however it was produced), and with the possibility of its application during surgery, to produce insensibility to pain. In his first letter to Knight, Hickman made it quite clear that he experimented on animals:

to ascertain the practicability of such treatment on the human subject.

Fig 10. Programme of Memorial Service at St. Mary's, Bromfield, 5th April 1930.
Courtesy of the Wellcome Trust Medical Photographic Library.

It was surely the practicability rather than the science of suspended animation that concerned him at that stage. His immediate concerns appeared to be with methodology and safety, not with principles of which he probably understood little. It must be said, however, that he left scant evidence of having thought deeply about the practicalities of inducing suspended animation in humans during surgery. Buxton did admit that Hickman's protocols:

…do not supply all the details of the experiments, though we are led to believe that true anaesthesia rather than asphyxia was one of the lines along which his investigations were conducted. His work with carbon dioxide was certainly along a correct path.

There is no doubt that in at least some of his experiments Hickman deliberately employed asphyxia, and almost certainly many of his experiments using carbonic acid gas involved appreciable oxygen deprivation. Nonetheless Buxton somehow read into Hickman's experiments that:

He was not content with suspended animation as an adjuvant to surgery for, as his experiments indicated, he wished to avoid all asphyxial complication, and so prevent haemorrhage.

Some of Buxton's paraphrasing may also be questioned. For example, compare the following two comments by Hickman with that of Buxton. In his address *To the Public* Hickman wrote:

He submits his observations and experiments to the public in the brief form of a letter to a private gentleman of the highest talent as a man of science who, with others thought them worthy to be laid before the Royal Society…

And in his open letter to Knight in the same pamphlet:

…some experiments which I have made lead me to …hope that you will think the results sufficiently interesting to induce you to do me the honour to lay them before the Royal Society.

Whereas Buxton wrote:

…although Hickman's friend, Mr T.A. Knight, was asked to bring the work before the Royal Society, we can discover no record of his paper being read or being received into the archives of that emporium of learning.

In considering whether Buxton intended to convey that Knight was Hickman's real or only his nominal friend, we should remember that the social context is in the 1820s. To have referred to T.A. Knight Esq. FRS of Downton Castle, a gentleman of high local standing and closely associated with two consecutive Presidents of the Royal Society (Sir Joseph Banks and Sir Humphry Davy), as the friend of a recently and minimally qualified young surgeon and son of a local farmer may, without qualifying evidence, give a misleading impression of the relationship.

The Text of the Souvenir

Hickman's birth, his marriage, his children, his admission as MRCS and as a Member of the Royal Medical Society of Edinburgh and his practice in Ludlow, Shifnal and Tenbury were reported in the main text. The information was provided by descendants of Hickman. The author of the *Souvenir's* text postulated that:

> ...*it is probable that Hickman's attention had been drawn to the work of another Shropshire doctor – Dr Thomas Beddoes – who was born at Shifnal in 1760...in support of this theory...the Faculty of the Edinburgh School...warmly supported Beddoes in his work. As Hickman was a member of the Edinburgh Medical Society, he may likely have known all about the current experiments of Beddoes, Davy, Faraday, Pearson, Warren and others of this period.*

If Hickman had read widely on the subject it is surprising that he did not quote or refer to a single authority.

Exhibits

As was to be expected the emphasis of the *Souvenir* was upon exhibits and the remainder of the text linked documents, illustrations and descriptions of exhibits, but with only minimal discussion. The exhibits are listed below. Items marked * were reproduced or illustrated in the *Souvenir*.

Letter to T.A. Knight, 21st February, 1824 * and accompanying descriptions of animal experiments *

Hickman's pamphlet *

Letter to Mrs Hickman, 21st April, 1828 (Published by F.F. Cartwright; 1952[5]) (see Chapter 6)

Copy or draft of Memorial to Charles X, 1828 * (the petition)

Facsimile of the registration of the receipt of Hickman's Memorial to Charles X and of its onward transmission to the Academy of Medicine *

Facsimile. Nomination...Dubois et al. (the date of 28th September in the *Souvenir* is probably erroneous) *

Letters from Thomas Dudley to Mrs Hickman in 1847: 24th January *; 11th March* 2nd April * 20th April * and 15th October * Four; one missing.

Copies from Medical Journals relating to Hickman (not identified in the *Souvenir* as individual exhibits)

Scales and weights used by Hickman *

Brass Door Plate * *(Now held in Science Museum Store)*

Notice Card (...Advice gratis to the Poor... &c.) *(Now held in Science Museum Store)*

Hickman's visiting card, used in Paris *

Flowered blue silk waistcoat worn by Hickman (*would fit someone a little over five feet tall; now in Science Museum Store*)

Portrait, copy in oils *

Watercolour (listed as an oil painting) commissioned by the Museum to portray Hickman experimenting in his 'laboratory'[6].

Oral evidence may have been solicited from Hickman's descendants, but if so no written record other than the bare personal details given above appear to have been kept, and no specific mention of this was included in the following acknowledgements:

> *For the help... received from all quarters... especially to Mrs Bettridge, of Tenbury, and Miss Blanche Thompson MPS of Birmingham, granddaughters of Henry Hill Hickman, who have contributed, by presentation or loan, valuable material. (figure 11, Thompson)*

Fig 11.
Miss Blanche Thompson (a granddaughter) also showing Hickman's pestle & mortar; now in the possession of Dr W.G.H. Leslie. *Courtesy of the Wellcome Trust Medical Photographic Library.*

The list of illustrations in the Contents of the *Souvenir* includes a miniature of Mrs Hickman, which is not included in the list of exhibits. (It is at the Tenbury Museum.) *(inside front cover)*

On the last page there are two illustrations not listed in the Contents: a photograph of the derelict family grave, and the inscription on the memorial tablet placed in the Bromfield Parish Church. The caption on the latter does not reveal that it was engraved by Eric Gill.

The following <u>extracts from Medical Journals</u> are included in the *Souvenir* but not mentioned in its Contents. These may indicate the identities of the above exhibited 'copies from Medical Journals relating to Hickman's work':

Bulletin de l'Académie Royale de Médecine Vol XII, 1846-1847 pp418-419. Meeting of 2nd March 1847 but referring back to 28th September (date probably erroneous). *Archives Generales de Médecine* Vol XVIII 1st series p. 453. Dudley T. *Letter* Lancet 6th February 1847 **i** p163. Dudley T. *Letter* Lancet 27th March 1847 **i** p345. Meeting Académie Royale de Médecine 23rd February 1847 and translation. M'Carthy D. *The Inventors of Ethereal Inhalation.* Medical Times 31st July, 1847 p. 454. Dudley T. *Letter* Medical Times 4th September 1847 Vol **XVI** p. 561.

References

1. Editorial. An unfinished chapter in the history of anaesthesia. *Brit. Med. J.* 1911; **ii**: 1434.
2. Simpson J.Y. *Works* Vol 2 Edinburgh A & C Black 1871.
3. Thompson C.J.S. Henry Hill Hickman: a forgotten pioneer of anaesthesia. *Brit. Med. J.* 1912; **i**: 843.
4. Buxton D.W. Those who worked in the dawn of anaesthesia. Henry Hill Hickman (1800-1829). *Brit. J. Anaesth.* 1926; **3**: 165.
5. Souvenir: *Henry Hill Hickman Centenary Exhibition 1830-1930.* London: Wellcome Foundation Ltd 1930.
6. Joyce F.W. A Forgotten Benefactor (correspondence). *Brit. Med. J.* 1927; **ii**: 471.
7. Layton F.G. A Forgotten Benefactor (correspondence). *Brit. Med. J.* 1927; **ii**: 567.
8. Mushin W.W. *Clinician versus researcher in anaesthesia.* In *Anaesthesia: Essays on its History* Ruprecht J., Lieburg M.J.V., Lee J.A., Erdmann W. eds. Berlin Heidelberg New York Tokyo Springer-Verlag 1985.
9. Hughes C. Hickman Memorial Fund (correspondence). *Ibid* 1929; **i**: 225.
10. Hughes C. Hickman Memorial Fund (correspondence). *Ibid* 1929; **ii**: 697.
11. Hughes C. Hickman Memorial Fund (correspondence). *Ibid* 1930; **i**: 363.
12. Annotation. *Ibid* 1930; **i**: 670.
13. Annotation. Henry Hill Hickman Centenary. *Ibid* 1930; **i**: 713.
14. Annotation. Research on Hickman. The Hickman Memorial. *Lancet* 1929; **i**: 787.
15. Editorial. Henry Hill Hickman. *Ibid;* 1929; **ii**: 1195.
16. Annotation. The Hickman Memorial. *Ibid;* 1930; **i**: 417.
17. Annotation. The Hickman Memorial. *Ibid;* 758.
18. Annotation. Henry Hill Hickman Memorial. *Ibid;* 775.
19. Annotation. Memorial to Henry Hill Hickman. *Ibid;* 832.
20. Editorial. *The Times.* 17th November 1928.
21. Hughes C. A Pioneer of Anaesthetics (correspondence). *The Times.* 3rd December 1928.
22. Leading Article. *The Times.* 3rd April 1930.
23. Lord Dawson of Penn. *Ibid.*
24. Collier J. The discovery of anaesthetics (correspondence). *The Times.* 5th April 1930.
25. Annotation. Anaesthetic Memorial and HH Hickman: pioneer in anaesthetic by inhalation. *The Times.* 7th April 1930.
26. Buxton D.W. XVIIIth International Medical Congress (correspondence). *Brit. Med. J.* 1913; **ii**: 208.
27. Anon. Benefactor Honoured. Important Ceremony at Bromfield. The unveiling of a Tablet. Centenary Tokens. *Ludlow Advertiser.* 12th April 1930.
28. Wellcome Trust: MS 7625.

CHAPTER EIGHT

The Verdict of History

Hickman's wife Eliza survived him by 23 years and thus lived to see the early days of ether anaesthesia. Within four months of its first public demonstration in Boston in 1846, she received a letter from a Thomas Dudley, of Kingswinford in the West Midlands:

Dear Madam,

You have probably seen Accounts of a new medical plan for inhaling aether in surgical operations. The Americans are claiming the invention, and I remember a similar system was proposed many years ago by your late husband. ... I think Dr Hickman wrote a pamphlet upon it, which was severely lashed in the Reviews.

If a copy of his work is in existence and you could allow me a view of it I wd. see that it was safely returned.

I think it no more than an act of common justice to assign the credit where it is justly due. ...

I consider he was very ill used because his system was condemned without examination – and if I remember right, it was nearly identical with the one wh. is now attracting universal attention. ...

Eliza evidently obliged because a letter from Dudley to *The Lancet* dated 6th February 1847 says:

... I am in a position to prove that a similar system was brought before the public nearly twenty years ago, by a Dr Hickman ... I am not prepared to state whether the inhaling system discovered by him was identical with the one now exciting such universal attention, but he most assuredly was the propounder of a system to produce insensibility to pain under operations by inhalation of some species of gas. ...

A copy of his memorial [to the King of France] is now before me, and also a letter from the widow of the memorialist ...

Unless [the present claimants] can prove that their discoveries were made anterior to the year 1828, the claim of priority must be awarded to Dr Hickman.

Dudley followed this up with a letter to Eliza dated 11th March:

Dear Madam,

I have your favour safe and the Pamphlet shall be taken every care of and returned.

I consider that Dr Hickman is clearly entitled to the claim of having originated the idea – and had his work been published in these more liberal times, the idea would have been followed up and probably the results of investigation would have been successful instead of the system being crushed as it was by unjust criticism without due inquiry.

65

Fig 12. 18 Teme Street, Tenbury Wells (2004) formerly Hickman's last home.

18 Teme Street.
Dr. Henry Hill Hickman
M.R.M.S.E. M.R.C.S.

The earliest pioneer of anaesthesia
by inhalation experimented and
practised in this building.

Born in Bromfield January 1800
Died in Tenbury April 1830
Buried at Bromfield Church

Honour a Physician with
the Honour due unto him.

Fig 13.
Close up of brass plate; beside the
entrance. MRMSE = Member of the
Royal Medical Society of Edinburgh,
not a qualification.

Both photographs by Dr Adrian Kuipers.

I shall again endeavour to call attention to the Pamphlet …

Dudley did so in another letter to *The Lancet* dated 27th March, but by 2nd April, there is a hint of resignation when he writes to Eliza:

…The case is now before the Public – nothing more can now be done …

and by 20th April, he had all but given up:

… It is clear the <u>principle</u> is his, but as the <u>Medium</u> was different, besides being open to objection, I think this will be laid hold of by the modern discoverers. I will file your transcripts for reference, in case of future need for it …

Later opinions
A spectrum of various published opinions and assessments of the place of Hickman in the history of anaesthesia are quoted in chronological order (with Denis Smith's comments in brackets).

<u>1912</u> *This young English surgeon … practically gave his life in his attempts to gain recognition for his discovery of a method of producing anaesthesia by inhalation.*

Thompson[1]

(It may have been premature to emphasize his desire for recognition when he was still trying to 'complete' his discovery in man).

<u>1927</u> *At the beginning of this century Hickman's name was partly recovered from obscurity by one or two of the leading medical journals …is it not reasonable to hope that those who represent the English Medical Faculty will do something to recognize the debt which we all owe to one of our greatest medical pioneers?* Joyce[2]

(It is not easy to define precisely what debt we owe to Hickman, yet it seems to have been Joyce's persistence that provided the spark that fired Hickman's Centenary celebrations).

<u>1930</u> *It is extremely difficult to appraise justly the work of Henry Hill Hickman, even to evaluate the man himself. Undoubtedly was it the great Principle – anaesthesia – for which his propaganda stood, as it was the development of that Principle which made for the aftermath – anaesthesia as we know it today. Hickman is the central figure, around him gradually have become grouped those things which have grown up in modern anaesthesia.* Buxton[3]

(One can imagine that Buxton may have had some difficulty in writing this).

Several Histories of Anaesthesia were published within a few years of Anaesthesia's accepted centenary of 16th October 1946, such as those by Fülöp-Miller[1] (*Fülöp-Miller introduced elements of fiction, speculation and wishful thinking into one of the early modern histories of anaesthesia. He did not indicate when he was doing so and thus misled some later authors*), Thomas Keys, Barbara Duncum and Howard Raper. The first appeared in 1938, the next four, published between 1945 and 1947, straddled the centenary. Some of these authors were particularly well placed to write histories of anaesthesia. For example, Keys was librarian at the Mayo Clinic and Associate Professor in the History of Medicine; Duncum worked in the Nuffield Department of Anaesthetics, Oxford, and before that at the Wellcome Historical Medical Museum and Raper was a dentist.

<u>1945</u> Thomas Keys, writing from the American perspective can afford to take a lofty view[5]:

It is hard to believe that the leading scientists of both England and France failed to recognise the contribution of Hickman or to investigate his claims scientifically. Even Sir Humphry Davy... failed to be impressed

(If only Davy had known about Hickman!)

<u>1947</u> *In 1824 Hickman unequivocally formulated the principle of general surgical anaesthesia by the inhalation of a gas.*   Duncum[6]

<u>1947</u> *His approach was clear-headed, definite, and scientific... Animals deprived of air in this way finally lost consciousness. But they had a pretty rough time before unconsciousness relieved them... He was certainly on the right track when he used carbon dioxide gas and it would be pleasant to report that he next used nitrous oxide gas. But there is nothing in the records to prove, or even to indicate strongly that he did, but this may be attributed to a natural impulse to round off a good story... If he had added oxygen to the carbon dioxide he would have had a fine anaesthetic mixture, one that came into limited use in 1914* [not traced by present author]. *It never seems to have occurred to him... Poor Hickman. He lived, dreamed, worked, died and was forgotten – not to be remembered until years later, after the introduction of anaesthesia by other men.*

Raper[7]

In <u>1952</u> Frederick Cartwright, an anaesthetist, did contribute some previously unpublished evidence on Hickman, and some fresh thinking in his book *The English Pioneers of Anaesthesia (Beddoes, Davy and Hickman)*. He began his twelve year task of gathering material for this around 1940, intending to write a history of anaesthesia from the English viewpoint, but finding Beddoes and Davy underrated and relatively neglected, he concentrated on them, adding two chapters on Hickman as next in logical sequence:

The valuation of Hickman's work must rely not upon what he may have done, but upon what he is known to have done... Surely his meaning is clear... insensibility was to be produced by the introduction of certain gases into the lungs to the point of asphyxia... His glory lies in the idea that lay behind his work.   Cartwright[8]

(The conclusion that the sole purpose of the gas administered was to produce asphyxia is debatable[9, 10]).

This was followed by Sykes's *Essays*:
<u>1960</u> *for pure originality of thought Hickman stands supreme. He alone conceived the idea without external stimuli of any kind... The amount of work he did was large considering his short life and his commitments as a general practitioner. But he did enough... to put him right at the top of the list, in spite of the fact that his work did not lead directly to any practical results.*   Sykes[11]

(In his opinion as to the relative importance of seven pioneers of anaesthesia, Sykes placed Hickman first. The other six he placed in the order Wells, Morton, Davy, Long, Simpson and Jackson, taking into account their originality, the amount of work they did and their attempts to publicise it, their luck and their courage).

And by Davison's *Evolution of Anaesthesia*:
<u>1965</u> *In 1824, Hickman published <u>A Letter on Suspended Animation</u>, in which he*

advocated anaesthesia with carbon dioxide and, in 1828 he applied through King Charles X, to the Royal Academy of Medicine in France. Hickman's proposal received no support, which was probably as well, since his method of anaesthesia was indubitably dangerous.

Davison[12]

These works give opinions on Hickman, formed from the limited evidence already available to their authors, without offering any fresh research. Some statements of implied 'fact' remain without validation, and some appear to be untrue. To give two pictorial examples, Plates XXV and XXVI in Volume 1 of Sykes' *Essays* are certainly not photographs of Hickman's recognised birthplace and of Knight's Downton Castle, which is what their captions claim them to be.

Even Cartwright's book, however, was not without errors of fact, such as his statement that Hickman was the only survivor of four children, and that Mr C.J.S. Thompson was the son of Dr F. Falconer Thompson who married one of Hickman's daughters. The two Thompsons were not related.

Perhaps the last word on Hickman should go to L.G. Stevenson, writing in the Bulletin of the History of Medicine in 1975[13]:

To foist a word he did not know on Hickman [i.e. anaesthesia] *whether we attach to it his concepts or our own, will not be helpful. But if we choose to say, with Hickman's greatest admirers, that he 'discovered' anaesthesia, the statement is not devoid of meaning. Columbus discovered America but thought he had penetrated to the Orient. The important difference is this: that America when once discovered by Columbus was never mislaid again. If the grown dog of Hickman's fifth experiment was anaesthetised and not asphyxiated, then Hickman was the far wandering Leif Ericson of our history of anaesthesia.*

References:

1. Thompson C.J.S. Henry Hill Hickman. A forgotten pioneer of anaesthesia. *Brit. Med. J.* 1912; **i**: 843.
2. Joyce F.W. A Forgotten Benefactor [Letter] *Brit. Med. J.* 1927; **ii**: 471.
3. Souvenir: *Henry Hill Hickman Centenary Exhibition 1830-1930.* London: Wellcome Foundation Ltd 1930.
4. Fülöp-Miller R. *Triumph over pain.* Translated by Eden & Cedar Paul. London: Hamish Hamilton 1938.
5. Keys T.E. *The History of Surgical Anesthesia* 2nd Ed. New York: Dover 1963.
6. Duncum B.M. *The Development of Inhalation Anaesthesia with special reference to the years 1846-1900* London: Wellcome Historical Medical Museum and Oxford University Press 1947. 2nd ed. London: Royal Society of Medicine Press Ltd on behalf of the History of Anaesthesia Society 1994.
7. Raper H.R. *Man against Pain: the Epic of Anesthesia* London: Gollancz 1947.
8. Cartwright F.F. *The English Pioneers of Anaesthesia (Beddoes, Davy & Hickman)* Bristol; John Wright & Sons, 1952.
9. Smith W.D.A. A history of nitrous oxide & oxygen anaesthesia; Part IVB. *Brit. J. Anaesth.* 1970; **42**: 445.
10. Smith W.D.A. A history of nitrous oxide & oxygen anaesthesia; Part IV. *Brit. J. Anaesth.* 1966; **38**: 58.
11. Sykes W.S. *Essays on the First Hundred Years of Anaesthesia.* Vol. 1 p.117-9 Edinburgh: Livingstone, 1960.
12. Davison M.H.A. *The Evolution of Anaesthesia.* Altrincham: John Sherratt and Son, 1965.
13. Stevenson L.G. Suspended animation and the history of anaesthesia. *Bull. Hist. Med.* 1975; **49**: 482-489.

APPENDIX A

<u>Text of a draft or of a copy of Henry Hickman's memorial to Charles X King of France dated at Paris, Hotel des Ambassadeurs, 11 Rue Notre Dame des Victoires, 1828 (*Courtesy; Wellcome Trust*)</u>

TO HIS MOST CHRISTIAN MAJESTY CHARLES X, KING OF FRANCE.
Sire,

In addressing Your Majesty upon a scientific subject of great importance to mankind, I feel properly humble, but a firm confidence in Your Majesty's universally known disposition to countenance valuable discoveries:- this relieves me from all apprehension of being considered presumptuous.

Permit me, Sire, to state that I am a British Physician, Member of the Royal College of Surgeons, London, who has visited Paris in part for the purpose of bringing to completion a discovery, to which I have been led by a course of observations and experiments on suspended animation.

This object has engaged my practical attention during several years: It appears demonstrable that the hitherto most agonizing, dangerous, and delicate surgical operations, may now be performed, with perfect safety, and exemption from pain, on brute animals in a state of suspended animation. Hence it is to be strongly inferred, by analogy, that the same salutary effects may be produced on the human frame, when rendered insensible by means of the introduction of certain gases into the lungs: I have discovered a number of facts connected with this important subject, and I wish to bestow them upon society.

Paris, the great Metropolis of Continental Europe, is the place above all others, where the profound studies of Humanity are, with the utmost facility, carried to their highest extent and perfection; and, Sire, I feel confident that I do not say too much, with a due regard for the scientific distinctions of my own Country, in avowing that these facilities, nowhere else to be found, and their most admirable results, have deservedly conferred on Your Majesty's Chief City, and its illustrious Schools of practical Philosophy, the eminent title of the Centre of Science to the Civilised World.

Presuming thus, Sire, to attract Your Majesty's thoughts to this interesting subject, I have resorted to the French Capital for the completion of my discovery, hoping to have the honour of placing it under Your Majesty's Royal and gracious auspices. In this manner I would pay to Your Majesty's Kingly and paternal Zeal in the promotion of every branch of useful knowledge that tributary homage which I am sure, Sire, it would be unjust, on a suitable occasion, to withhold from an Exemplary Monarch, who is surrounded by the wise and the Learned, the philanthropic and celebrated in all the Arts and Sciences, which benefit, ameliorate, ornament and dignify the condition of mankind.

It is upon purposes of this nature Sire, that Your Majesty daily deigns and delights to smile with enlightened and condescending encouragement. Your Majesty invites the philosophical from all Lands and they are certain of protection.

It must have occurred to Your Majesty's magnanimous mind, that our species rise in the scale of moral and intellectual greatness, in proportion as our efforts are directed to the diminution of the sum of human misery, and physical evil. This was the elevated and virtuous aim of the Sages, and the best of Kings of Antiquity; and this grand purpose is yet more conspicuous in modern times:

Under this grave and powerful impression, I have ventured on the liberty of praying Your Majesty to be pleased, by an express intimation, or command, on the subject, to permit me to develop my ideas on operations in a state of suspended animation, in the presence of Your Majesty's Medical and Surgical Schools, that I may have the benefit of their eminent and assembled talent, and emulous cooperation.

It is also my desire, at a fit opportunity, to solicit the honour of presenting to Your Majesty, in person, if Your Majesty will condescend to receive it, a Book containing an account of my discovery which as far as I know or can learn, has entirely originated with myself; and should my labours meet with the approbation of Charles The Tenth, I shall ever enjoy the grateful satisfaction of believing that I have devoted myself to my profession to a distinguished and to a happy end.

With the hope that Providence may continue Your Majesty's invaluable Health, and prosper Your Illustrious Reign,

I have the honour to be, Sire, with profound Respect Your Majesty's

Most Obedient and Most Humble Servant.

H. HICKMAN

APPENDIX B

Descriptions of Henry Hickman's NOTEBOOK and LEDGER. (By courtesy of Dr W.G.H. Leslie).
Complete photocopies held by the Wellcome Trust.

NOTEBOOK 1816

General description
Vellum, hard back 21 x 33 x 3cm. Marked faintly in ink on spine: 'No.2' (presumably there was another notebook marked No.1). In ink on front cover: 'H. Hickman. 1816'. Watermark 1813
After the fly- and the first leaf, the pages are numbered 1 to 203. Writing ends on p.202. The final 11 leaves and the rear flyleaf are blank. Contains an estimated 50,000 words.

Text: Except for entries under 'Brookes's Anatomy' or under 'Observations and Experiments' the contents appear to comprise notes taken from textbooks. Direct comparison has been made of the texts in his notebook and in textbooks under 'Cullen's Practice of Physic' and Erasmus Darwin's 'Zoonomia'. Hickman's text has mostly been copied word for word however a single paragraph of Hickman's text is often made up from a fusion of parts of more than one paragraph of the printed text with intervening paragraphs sometimes skipped. This was done intelligently and it is not obvious from reading Hickman's text alone. Plotting page numbers in Hickman's notebook against page numbers for same subject matter in Cullen's Practice of Physic shows that Hickman became increasingly economical with words. There are very few errors and few words have been deleted or inserted. This suggests that even if he did not write an initial rough copy he at least sketched out fairly detailed preliminary guide notes – unless he was copying out someone else's notes. This was presumably produced as an educational exercise and for reference; but it might also have proved useful as evidence of work done, perhaps for example when seeking admission to take the MRCS exam.

Hickman's notes were under the following headings:
p. 1   Cullen's Practice of Physic
p. 42   Fordyce on Fever
p. 55   Denman's Midwifery
p. 67   Wilson on Febrile Diseases
p. 80   Essays on Consumption by Dr Beddoes
p. 82   Hunter on the Venereal Disease
p. 89   Clarke on Female Diseases
p. 98   Adams on Morbid Poisons
p.110   Currie's Medical Reports
p.114   Diseases of the Generative System by Roberton [*Advertised as on sale in Berrows Worcester Journal on 30.9.1813*]
p.132   Mathias on the Mercurial Disease – 1816

p.135   Brookes's Anatomy (*No published book traced*). in Left Hand Margin: 'January 19th 1818' [*A Monday*] in Right Hand Margin: 'First Course'

p.136   near bottom left margin: 'January 21st 1818'

p.137   Main Heading: 'Operations'

p.138-142 have dates: January 22nd-31st

p.144   Mathias on the Mercurial Disease

p.160   Darwin's Zoonomia.

Evidently Hickman was attending a two-week course of Surgical Anatomy at Joshua Brookes' Theatre of Anatomy, Blenheim Street Gt. Marlborough Street, London from 19th to 31st January, [27th was his eighteenth birthday].

Hickman's text covering Brookes Anatomy amounts to about 1,750 words. The marginal sub-headings are: Aneurysm; Hypogastric Artery; Femoral Artery; Posterior Tibial Artery; Arteria Peronea Communis; Arteria Tibialis Anticus; Lingual Artery; Hernia Scrotalis or Cystocele – you should not divide the sac at all, in operating, but take off the stricture and return it; Abdominal Hernia; Hernia Femoralis; Difference of Retention & Suppression of Urine; Mr Brookes has some most beautiful preparations of Hydatides in the Kidneys and Bladder; Lithotomy; Compression of the Brain; Trephine; Amputation; First practised by Brookes; Hip Joint; Fistula Lacrymali.

Transcriptions

At the foot of page 109, Hickman wrote:

A. 'I have been much pleased with the arguments of Dr Adams in favour of Hunter's doctrine and have read his work with great satisfaction.'

B. Observations & Experiments

Mr Jukes thinks that after large and repeated bloodlettings in inflammation of the brain that narcotics in small doses are followed by the very best effects- - - Mr Jukes thinks that in treating a disease the digestive powers ought always to be attended to for how is it possible, he observes, to keep up a healthy action in a part while disease is going on in these organs, and he thinks that every uncomfortable feeling to which the human body is liable, may originate in His [?] disease. Mr Jukes thinks that whenever headache comes on in pregnant women, or during the time of labour, blood should always be taken away as permanent blindness may come on, if blood letting is neglected, which circumstance occurred in a Patient of Mr Lee's - - - - - Mr Jukes thinks that no medical aid is of use where alteration of structure has taken place in parts that cannot be got at - - - - - - - - - - - - - - - - - - Dr Philip has found by experiment that Galvanism has a great effect on Digestion and Asthma. - - - - -Mr Watson thinks that Opium has injurious effects, in gastritis, which I have seen in a patient of his, ordered by Dr Jones - Mr Jukes believes that all pain is in proportion to the power of resistance in the muscular fibre, if the resistance is great the pain is excessive if not it is in a less degree, therefore persons in health cannot bear pain so well as those whose muscular power has been diminished by ill health - - - - - - - - - - - - - - Mr Jukes tells me that Rea & Cannadry Gardeners in Town, assured him that they have found from experience that whenever Peach Trees are moved into a new situation the soil should be completely changed as they have never found a Peach Tree do well when placed in a new situation and same soil of one that had been removed, and they likewise state that in cultivating primroses the soil should be changed every two years; and that to procure fine celeri, after it has been sown, it should be transplanted three or four times before it is put in the trenches; all which facts I think are very worthy of notice to the gardner - - - - - - - - - - - -

Mr Carden asserts from his own observation that stimulants are the best applications to burns within twelve hours after the accident. - - - - - - - - - - - -

Mr Ware has written in favour of the efficacy of electricity and mercurial snuff in cases of Amaurosis; and that the pupil has been generally dilated, in the cases benefited by electricity - - - - - - - - - - - - - O'Halloran. This gentleman very justly observes that the most expert operator is not the best surgeon as we must in many cases rather avoid than perform capital operations and that it is not enough for a surgeon to know how to operate but he must also know how [?] to do it.

PoH [O'Halloran?] & Sharp. says that he has seen many limbs amputated in which gangrene had begun to show itself but never saw it succeed; invariably hastening the patient's death though the skin above the mortified part may appear sound yet the muscles which it covers and those round the bones may be in a state of gangrene, therefore till the mortification is stopt, amputation is useless, the stump always assuming gangrene - - - - - - - - - - - - - - - -

Comments

i) 'Observations and Experiments' are of particular note for the names mentioned. Richard Jukes and Kenrick Watson, partners of 23 and 24 Bridge Street, Stourport-on-Severn, which is twelve miles from Worcester, had as their apprentice for eighteen months from 14th September 1810, Charles Hastings, founder of the British Medical Association. He was $16\frac{3}{4}$ years when apprenticed at a fee of £157:10/- for two years. Hastings was also directed to Brookes' School of Anatomy in London. In December, 1812, when not quite 19 years old he was appointed House Surgeon at Worcester Infirmary (see McMenemey *The Life and Times of Sir Charles Hastings* 1959). (Hickman was not recorded as being at the Worcester Infirmary).

ii) On 5th January, 1818, John Foxton and Kenrick Watson, surgeons, certified on an indenture that "Mary Mason the apprentice within named is not able to perform her business as an apprentice by reason of lameness we do therefore hereby discharge him the within named John Hickman from the covenant of the within indenture of apprenticeship..." John Hickman is described as of Lady Halton, which identifies him as Henry Hickman's father. John Foxton was a surgeon of Broad Street, Ludlow and as a local man it is not surprising to see his name on the indenture, but it is not obvious why a surgeon based twenty-five miles away in Stourport should be also be named. Watson may have joined Foxton because he happened to be there for some other reason. If Hickman had served as Watson's apprentice, then Watson may have been reporting on progress and advising about his career. Hickman might even have accompanied him to Lady Halton, where he was born, as 5th January was only a couple of weeks before Joshua Brookes' Course in Anatomy. In an 1821 case report, Hickman referred to Dr Gervaise Thorpe, a Ludlow Physician, as his friend. Conjecturing further, if Hickman had discussed a surgical career with this friend, Thorpe might have consulted John Foxton who could have recommended Kenrick Watson. Foxton had two sons of Hickman's generation who trained at St. George's Hospital.

Dr Wilson Philip (who engaged in animal experiments) was a physician and Mr Carden was a surgeon, at Worcester Infirmary. Ware, Lee, Jones, O'Halloran or Sharp have not been identified. Except for Dr Philip, none of these medics published anything that Hickman would have been likely to copy into his notebook. One is left with the impression that Hickman was present when Mr Jukes 'thinks' (see above), perhaps in the relationship of Master and apprentice, perhaps at a local medical society meeting. (There was one based on Worcester at this period). The wording seems to imply that Hickman was in the presence of the people named when they 'thought' etc. In one instance there seemed to be a direct encounter: "Mr Jukes tells me..."

LEDGER 1829-1830

General description:
Green leather bound hardback 17 x 45 x 3.5 cm. Spine: gold lettered LEDGER, red background with gold decorated borders. Flyleaf: marked in ink 'J/n 12/-'. Facing flyleaf: in pencil, '19'. Index follows flyleaf:

14 leaves hand lettered in paired capitals, black and red alternating, no letters J and U. Remaining 166 leaves: blue feint rule, left red margin and right single cash columns, on both sides of leaves. Entries: first 47 sides hand numbered in ink. All these and following sides contain entries. No other entries or marks.

Period covered: July 1829-March 1830, the last nine months of Hickman's life and probably the whole period of his practice in Tenbury. Over sixty patients named *including John & Benjamin Hickman in Ludlow*. Entries increased around end of first week in September and remained level until 23rd March when there was a sharp fall 10 days before Hickman died (April 2nd). New patients were most numerous in September and December but fell to a lower level in January and February. In March they were as few as in the previous July. Visits for which a charge was made were frequent in January but also fairly frequent in December and February. Actual drugs supplied were not stated (entries as 'Bolusses 1/6, Mixture 2/6, Pills 2/6' etc.).

Letter addressed to Miss Gardner, Leigh Court, nr. Worcester from Edinburgh 21st Sept 1819, 5 Nicolson Street. (Courtesy Dr W.G.H. Leslie – a copy is held by the Wellcome Trust).

My Dearest Eliza,

It is now 12 o'clock when silence reigns through the whole house and when the thoughts of your Henry invariably stray to Leigh Court but more particularly after receiving a letter he did this morning which made him happier than he has been for some time past in as much as it has so thoroughly convinced him of his Eliza's attachment and that the impression the words of his dear mother (for such I shall ever call her) had left are entirely removed though at the time I well knew the meaning of her injunctions as being those of a mother and one anxious in my welfare, but notwithstanding all this, my fears were many lest any chance should deprive me of all I value on earth though this I aknowledge to be a foolish idea when I know her heart to be as constant as it is virtuous – as it is honourable – words, Eliza, I cannot find to express the pleasurable feelings I had from your mother's part of the letter in which I find your preference for me above all others exemplified though decency I suppose prevented your telling me the manner in which it was shown, but remember my dear Girl, I am well aware that it is nothing but you must expect to meet with and I to hear, so that you trust, will commit to paper (if not at one time at another) every thing that passes and be assured that I will not again excuse a short letter for you must know that anything is agreeable from you even the straying imagination that may attend you during the time of writing. I expect to meet Charles Stephenson with a long face but I hope not with a pistol, being an instrument I very much dislike, particularly when I think on you, though I don't know but your cause would induce me to take one sooner than any other if insulted. I was much pleased with my highland excursion and in a general way with the Scotch manner but in one respect I thought them rather too forward, an instance of which (if you promise not to think me vain) I will tell you but I must confess it is rather an odd subject and one I hardly know how to begin about, as you know I never on any occasion fall in love – however to be plain it is that a Scotch heiress fell violently in love with some of my qualifications (for which or what I don't know but must ask you) and immediately wished to ensnare me to the bonds of matrimony, making me proprietor of highland property. Here I thought was a complete reversion in the order of Nature and wished that my dear Eliza (that worlds could not induce me to forget or dishonour) had been by to have heard my declaration – riches may go well with the caprice and fashion of the world but they do not add one tittle to happiness and domestic comfort which can arise solely from long and sincere affection which I trust and think (no doubt remains) has existed between us and in consideration thereof gave a pointed denial to all parties. Thus far your case and mine have resembled each other. It is probable, and I think most likely that C.S. will write you in hopes of holding correspondence, if so, I hope you will make a proper apology and return the letter which method is certainly the most proper step a young woman (in your situation) can take, at once showing yourself to be another's, though after he sees me he will have more sense and honour thus to expose himself, at least I hope so – I have entered here another quarter as I cannot find lodging half so comfortable and being rather an invalid think I cannot better myself, but this Stevenson and I shall talk when we meet. I am like you wish the time would fly as fast again as it does but I think if I keep well you must give me leave to stray from you till July or August as I want to finish all my examinations etc before I return though if you wish me particularly to come back by land <u>it is possible I may bend my course towards the neighbourhood of Worcester</u> but on <u>what account</u> I leave you to judge, it being impossible that <u>I</u> can. Now for ——[?] sentences for want of room. I have begun a letter to your Aunt Deakin. I shall write to my father tomorrow. Edinburgh is very dull. I hope for and expect a letter weekly from Miss Gardner, Leigh Court. I am better in health but not well. Give my kindest regards to Ben and tell him to write me and to Humphrey – and with every sentiment of affection to your dear Father and Mother, believe me your ever affectionate with a kiss

H.H.HICKMAN

P.S. Remember me to Miss Fox

<u>On address page</u>.
You never said whether your father has received the papers I have sent weekly for this month past. When I write you I always blame the paper manufacturers for not making larger sheets. I have a gentleman who comes to consult the professors here for ill health and having accidently met with him he thinks from the explanation I have given him of his case that I understand it better than they and accordingly has put himself under my care. It is of longstanding and an obstinate case, but I shall make him well. Be sure write an early answer and give a long letter for you must be aware by this time that this is particularly short which from me you like, I am sure, better than a long one. Heaven Bless you. Good night, rather good morning being half past one o'clock – and lastly write.

*   *   *   *   *   *

<u>Text of a letter addressed to Mrs H. Hickman, Corve Street, Ludlow; postmark 'Worcester, 1823,' from her mother, Mrs E.C. Gardner.</u>

My Dear Eliza,
We have been expecting Henry at Cotheridge ever since last Friday week and we are wondering what can have prevented him; but I hope he has some <u>profitable employment</u> at home. Your father saw Mr Bearcroft on Sunday, he said his little girl is certainly better, but the amendment is but slow, he was very anxious to know when Henry was likely to come into this neighbourhood. I have got one of the <u>cheap</u> <u>dresses</u> for you. I think it will be very <u>suitable</u> for The Hyde. I should think Kitty would make it very well for you. Jane has one, and it really looks very well when made up. I should have sent it by the coach, but thought the carriage would be almost as much as the gown cost for it is as much as ——[?]d. a yd. Your father said he thought you told him something about Breakfast Powder; if you want let me know and I will send it together. Ben came here last Wednesday week and stayed till last Tuesday. He met Mr Godson on the Monday at the Badham's when everything was arranged for us to have The Hyde. Ben is to be Tenant. Mr Godson behaved very well. He and Mr Badham consulted together about the [Reading?] property and they agreed to my dividing it with the creditors. Mr Godson said he wishes to avoid all Law Suits, and he should recommend the Creditors coming into the terms proposed and he had no doubt but they would do so. I rather think The Hyde will be given up to us. I have begun packing up, as I have a good deal to do I must get on with a little every day. I forgot to tell you that Mr Badham

has promised Ben if the business is not quite settled with Mr Dixon by the time we are to go to The Hyde he will advance some money to begin with. I am sure you will be concerned to hear of the death of poor Mary Downer, she died on Saturday morning. And poor Mrs Dudley of Shut End died last week. I wish you to put on slight mourning for these. Mrs D. was a most worthy woman and the Dudley family are some of the nearest relatives I have on my mother's side. I hope Henry will come here as soon as he possibly can as Miss Bearcroft is getting a little better, it will be a sad pity for her to be neglected. If he is not likely to come this week write and let me know about the Breakfast Powder. We intend going to The Hyde as soon as the sale is over but I will let you know as soon as we have fixed the day. I expect Ben will be here this day fortnight. I must now conclude as your Father is going to Worcester and will take this. He unites with me and your Aunt in best love to you both. I remain my dearest Eliza

Yours truly affectionate mother

E.C. GARDNER.

*   *   *   *   *   *

APPENDIX D

Hickman Medallists

Fig 14. Obverse of the Hickman Medal.
Designed by T.H. Paget. Reverse shows a beautiful woman
with the inscription: 'Anaesthesia Victrix Dolorum'.
By kind permission of the RSM Archives.

Recipients of the Hickman Medal

1935	Wesley Bourne	1971	Cecil Gray
1938	Sir Ivan Magill	1974	Alfred Lee
1941	Arthur Guedel	1977	W.W. Mushin
1944	Ralph Waters	1981	Andrew Hunter
1947	Sir Robert Macintosh	1984	Derek Wylie
1950	R.J. Minnitt	1987	Philip Bromage
1953	John Gillies	1990	G. Jackson Rees
1956	Harold Griffith	1993	Brian Sellick
1959	Michael Nosworthy	1996	John Nunn
1962	Ronald Woolmer	1999	William Mapleson
1965	C. Langton Hewer	2003	Archibald Brain
1968	James Raventos		